The
FOUR RULES
OF NUMBER
BOOK 1

by
K. A. HESSE

TEACHER'S EDITION

LONGMAN

The following quotations were fairly obvious and easy to write. This book is designed to make them easy to carry out in everyday practice.

Children should have constant and varied drill in all the basic facts of addition, subtraction, multiplication and division, so that these are known absolutely . . .

It is a common experience that some children appear to master the first steps of a new process, but fail to achieve command of a new skill. This is usually an indication that the process has not been analysed into the many short steps that children of no more than average ability require.

Arithmetic in Primary Schools

Dr Fleming points out that the findings of research show that the acquisition of practice on isolated difficulties and processes is more helpful than practice on mixed material. Hence she suggests that much experience with isolated difficulties in small sums is better than the attempted solution of a smaller number of unwieldy calculations of greater complexity.

Miss Mary Atkinson in *Junior School Community*

Much time may be saved if the mental habits that each new rule imparts are considered separately . . . Mechanical drill work should be purposeful . . .

There is no need for the child to write down every exercise that he attacks . . .

The written rules are best regarded as forms of mental technique or as complex habits to be formed. To teach them successfully means that the child will acquire, with the least expenditure of time and energy, such a degree of speed and accuracy that they can be readily applied.

Ministry of Education Handbook of Suggestions for Teachers

FOREWORD

Many children fail to make the progress in arithmetic of which they are capable because they never master some elementary number combination or some quite simple stage or stages in the four basic rules of number. Unless such specific weakness is precisely detected by the teacher, it is likely to persist as a handicap right through schooldays into adult life. At school this specific weakness can easily hold back progress in arithmetic so much that it produces a sense of defeatism about the subject; the consequent feeling of failure often spreads and proves a depressing influence on other branches of school work. The handicap prejudices the child's vocational prospects, and in adult life causes a wholly disproportionate nuisance and inefficiency in shop or office or factory as well as in ordinary everyday affairs.

Yet all this can and frequently does arise because the specific weaknesses have never been detected. First they must be diagnosed, then they must be remedied. In this book the "check" pages provide the means of diagnosis, and for each possible weakness extensive remedial work is supplied, finely graded as regards to difficulty.

USE IN THE PRIMARY SCHOOL

Ideally, any weaknesses should be nipped in the bud—that is, in the particular stage of the Primary school where it is first liable to develop. This book is accordingly designed for regular and systematic use, as the essential companion to any other arithmetic book or class teaching.

Its value at this stage arises from two important principles.

(*a*) It makes sure that *every* number combination or bond is practised at every stage. Surprisingly many weaknesses arise from the chance that a particular textbook, excellent in other ways, may give little or even no practice in a particular number combination.

(*b*) It guarantees systematic progress by sorting out the problems in every process into fine grades of difficulty.

The book can accordingly be used with great advantage in every class of the Primary school. With the brighter children it guards against the constant risk that apparently rapid progress is masking a particular and easily correctible weakness. With the weaker children it guarantees that only one new type of difficulty is introduced in a new exercise and that enough practice is given, so that the child is always stepping forward confidently with a continued sense of achievement.

USE IN THE SECONDARY SCHOOL

The value of this to every secondary school is that it is both diagnostic and remedial. If there are any weaknesses in the basic rules of number, then the sooner they are found out the better, before more damage is done and more time is wasted by both child and teacher.

If the "check" pages of this book are given to every new entry form, it will be rare indeed if no weaknesses are detected. Each particular weakness can be remedied and corrected by using the exercise designed to give adequate practice at the precise point of difficulty diagnosed.

With backward children this book can be used with remedial coaching groups in the way suggested on page v.

How to Use

THE CHECK PAGES

<table>
<tr><td colspan="2">Where to find the
CHECK PAGES</td></tr>
<tr><td>ADDITION</td><td>on page 1</td></tr>
<tr><td>SUBTRACTION</td><td>18</td></tr>
<tr><td>MULTIPLICATION</td><td>31</td></tr>
<tr><td>Long Multiplication</td><td>44</td></tr>
<tr><td>DIVISION</td><td>48</td></tr>
<tr><td>Long Division</td><td>67</td></tr>
</table>

Each row in a check page is *diagnostic*.
Each row contains a key to the *remedy*.

Each check page must be worked row by row
ACROSS THE PAGE
and should usually be marked
ROW BY ROW

The six check pages in this book are the keys for teacher and pupil alike in getting the most value out of it. Their use can be easily explained to a class, and thereafter the device is so simple that each child can use the pages to provide his or her own discipline of work, with the teacher knowing all the time exactly what stage the child has reached and what difficulty is holding up progress.

There is one check page for each rule. Each check page does two things:—

it shows precisely *what goes wrong*
and it shows what is needed to *put it right*.

On each check page there is one row of questions for each stage of difficulty.

If questions in any one row are answered wrongly, the printed reference at the end of the row tells teacher and pupil alike where to find further practice in the precise difficulty that is holding up progress.

The difficulty may be persistent muffing of particular number combinations. This is shown up by apparently random mistakes irrespective of the difficulty of the process. *Diagnosis* of failure in specific number combinations is of the utmost importance; difficult with the ordinary textbook, quite simple with this check page. The *remedy* is rapid practice with a TABLE of appropriate number combinations. Example:—

						Further Practice	
						Table	Pages
A	1 +2 **3**	3 +0 **3**	2 +5 **7**	24 +63 **86**	42 +57 **99**	1	2 & 3

Here is the mistake.　Here is the remedy: quick practice of a number of number combinations.

Or the difficulty may be an inability to master a further complication in the process itself. *Diagnosis* is provided by general failure in a particular row following general success in previous rows. *E.g.*, addition of units may be generally good, but the carrying of tens may not be understood. The *remedy* is explanation of this specific difficulty and more practice on it. Example:—

						Further Practice	
						Table	Pages
B	5 +16 **21**	3 +18 **11**	4 +26 **30**	48 +22 **60**	59 +38 **107**	2	4 & 5

Here are the mistakes.　Here is the remedy: more practice in this stage of the process-carrying.

iv

USING THE CHECK PAGES FOR INDIVIDUAL AND GROUP WORK

(Alternative Check pages are printed on pages 72–78)

The check pages provide the control pages for individual progress. They have the double advantage that the child knows what to do next, *and* the teacher can see at a glance what the child is doing.

For individual, group, and class work, the check page should be *worked and marked one row at a time*. If there are no errors in a particular row, the child is ready to proceed to the next row. If there are errors in a particular row, the child is directed, by the printed instruction at the end of the row, to the appropriate table or exercise for more practice before proceeding to the new complication presented by the next row. After further practice, the child can check whether the particular difficulty has been mastered by trying the row on the check page again and getting it completely right before proceeding to the next row on the check page.

(If only a short period of practice is needed, it may be advisable to give the child on the second check the *alternative* check page at the end of this Teacher's Edition.)

USING THE CHECK PAGES WITH A NEW CLASS

— to find out what *stage* they have reached,
— to determine what *revision* is necessary,
— to sort them into *groups* for revision and new work,
— to detect particular difficulties of *individuals*.

For these purposes the new class is given the whole of one check page to work through. (If the class is one that should have already learnt all the Four Rules of Number, then the *Combined* check page—provided on the last page of this Teacher's Edition—can be given first, following this up where necessary with further analysis by use of the appropriate check pages in the Pupil's Edition.)

The whole class should start at the beginning of the check page with row A, and work across the page row by row. Each individual will go on until he or she comes to a halt or is clearly getting more sums wrong than right in a particular row.

No time limit should usually be set when the check page is used for these purposes, and each individual should be encouraged to work as far as possible. It is, however, useful if each child records the exact time when he or she comes to a halt or is stopped by the teacher because of general failure at some stage. This time check helps to sort out in the class both (*a*) those who may be inclined to rush ahead at the expense of carefulness, and (*b*) those whose work is fairly accurate but too slow—an indication frequently of lack of confidence or insufficient practice. "In mechanical exercises brisk working should be encouraged" (*Ministry of Education Handbook of Suggestions for Teachers*).

THE PURPOSE OF THE TABLES

All the practice in the simple but fundamental number combinations or bonds is given in clearly labelled tables, each of which is enclosed in a ruled frame. This has been done for two reasons.

For *Remedial work*, diagnosis from the check page often shows a certain facility with the process but a persistent muffing of some particular number combination. It is advisable to overcome these specific shortcomings by specific work uncomplicated by the difficulties of the process. It is also advisable to do this work as fast as possible, as this work is essentially a memory exercise. Hence, suggested times are indicated for all tables.

For *Class teaching*, the tables provide preparatory work for tackling the next stage or complication of the process. They provide a preliminary canter through those number combinations that will be met in the exercises on this next stage, and so conserve later the child's concentration for the specific new difficulty in the process.

A further note on the tables appears on page 71.

CONTENTS

vi

viii

The
FOUR RULES
OF NUMBER
BOOK 1

K. A. HESSE

LONGMAN

LONGMAN GROUP UK LIMITED
Longman House,
Burnt Mill, Harlow, Essex CM20 2JE, England
and Associated Companies throughout the world.

© Longman Group Ltd 1956

First published 1956
Thirtieth impression 1989

Pupils' edition   ISBN 0-582-18009-0

Teachers' edition   ISBN 0-582-18010-4

Produced by Longman Group (FE) Ltd
Printed in Hong Kong

Work across the page

						Further Practice
					Table	Pages

A

1	3	2	24	42	1	2 & 3
+2	+0	+5	+63	+57		
3	3	7	87	99		

B

5	3	4	48	59	2	4 & 5
+16	+18	+26	+22	+38		
21	21	30	70	97		

C

11	11	12	26	35	2	6
12	10	21	30	4		
13	26	17	7	45		
36	47	50	63	84		

D

22	43	25	20	58	2	7 to 9
13	20	10	34	7		
15	54	75	46	82		
50	117	110	100	147		

E

32	25	23	89	69	3	10 & 11
13	46	56	86	98		
47	80	88	25	4		
92	151	167	200	171		

F

47	58	374	338	658	4	12 to 14
26	73	105	80	99		
57	69	268	572	876		
130	200	747	990	1633		

G

123	65	273	463	413	5	15 & 16
243	373	647	97	69		
115	400	89	84	907		
425	197	675	406	86		
906	1035	1684	1050	1475		

H

386	342	1384	6768	5785	6	17
576	153	2678	4889	8599		
989	265	1769	70	607		
78	104	3007	586	88		
2029	376	2898	909	7895		
	1240	11736	13222	22974		

See pages iv and v for suggestions on how best to use this page. An alternative check page for addition is printed on page 72 of the Teacher's Edition.

ADDITION TABLE: 1
Work across the page

Time for Table
4 minutes.

Add (**+**):

A	$1+1=2$	$1+0=1$	$0+1=1$	$0+0=0$	$2+1=3$
B	$1+2=3$	$2+0=2$	$0+2=2$	$2+2=4$	$3+0=3$
C	$3+1=4$	$1+3=4$	$3+2=5$	$0+3=3$	$4+1=5$
D	$2+3=5$	$4+0=4$	$5+1=6$	$1+5=6$	$5+0=5$
E	$4+2=6$	$1+4=5$	$3+3=6$	$6+1=7$	$5+2=7$
F	$2+4=6$	$1+6=7$	$0+6=6$	$4+3=7$	$3+4=7$
G	$2+5=7$	$1+7=8$	$7+1=8$	$8+1=9$	$1+8=9$
H	$5+3=8$	$6+2=8$	$4+4=8$	$3+5=8$	$2+6=8$
I	$6+3=9$	$5+4=9$	$2+7=9$	$7+2=9$	$3+6=9$
J	$3+4=7$	$0+9=9$	$4+5=9$	$9+0=9$	$2+7=9$

Add (**+**):

A

| $\begin{array}{r}1\\+1\\\hline2\end{array}$ | $\begin{array}{r}2\\+2\\\hline4\end{array}$ | $\begin{array}{r}1\\+2\\\hline3\end{array}$ | $\begin{array}{r}1\\+3\\\hline4\end{array}$ | $\begin{array}{r}0\\+1\\\hline1\end{array}$ | $\begin{array}{r}0\\+0\\\hline0\end{array}$ | $\begin{array}{r}2\\+1\\\hline3\end{array}$ | $\begin{array}{r}1\\+0\\\hline1\end{array}$ |

B

| $\begin{array}{r}1\\+4\\\hline5\end{array}$ | $\begin{array}{r}2\\+3\\\hline5\end{array}$ | $\begin{array}{r}0\\+4\\\hline4\end{array}$ | $\begin{array}{r}1\\+5\\\hline6\end{array}$ | $\begin{array}{r}2\\+4\\\hline6\end{array}$ | $\begin{array}{r}3\\+1\\\hline4\end{array}$ | $\begin{array}{r}3\\+0\\\hline3\end{array}$ | $\begin{array}{r}2\\+5\\\hline7\end{array}$ |

C

| $\begin{array}{r}1\\+7\\\hline8\end{array}$ | $\begin{array}{r}0\\+6\\\hline6\end{array}$ | $\begin{array}{r}7\\+0\\\hline7\end{array}$ | $\begin{array}{r}2\\+6\\\hline8\end{array}$ | $\begin{array}{r}6\\+2\\\hline8\end{array}$ | $\begin{array}{r}3\\+4\\\hline7\end{array}$ | $\begin{array}{r}4\\+4\\\hline8\end{array}$ | $\begin{array}{r}4\\+3\\\hline7\end{array}$ |

D

| $\begin{array}{r}2\\+7\\\hline9\end{array}$ | $\begin{array}{r}3\\+5\\\hline8\end{array}$ | $\begin{array}{r}5\\+2\\\hline7\end{array}$ | $\begin{array}{r}3\\+6\\\hline9\end{array}$ | $\begin{array}{r}4\\+5\\\hline9\end{array}$ | $\begin{array}{r}0\\+9\\\hline9\end{array}$ | $\begin{array}{r}3\\+3\\\hline6\end{array}$ | $\begin{array}{r}7\\+1\\\hline8\end{array}$ |

50 of the simplest addition combinations—practice in the change from horizontal to vertical method of layout.

Add (+):

A

```
  4      3      5      4      3      6      5
+ 1    + 2    + 1    + 2    + 5    + 3    + 4
———    ———    ———    ———    ———    ———    ———
  5      5      6      6      8      9      9
```

B

```
 1 1    1 2    1 0    2 1    2 2    4 0    6 3
+1 2   +1 1   +1 1   +1 3   +4 5   +3 8   +3 4
————   ————   ————   ————   ————   ————   ————
 2 3    2 3    2 1    3 4    6 7    7 8    9 7
```

C

```
 1 2    1 3    1 3    3 2    1 5    5 2    2 0
+5 4   +7 5   +8 6   +3 3   +4 3   +2 3   +7 9
————   ————   ————   ————   ————   ————   ————
 6 6    8 8    9 9    6 5    5 8    7 5    9 9
```

D

```
 2 4    4 1    3 4    5 4    6 2    5 5    3 3
+5 2   +5 8   +2 1   +1 4   +2 6   +4 3   +3 5
————   ————   ————   ————   ————   ————   ————
 7 6    9 9    5 5    6 8    8 8    9 8    6 8
```

E

```
 2 3    1 3    2 6    1 4    3 4    5 4    5 3
+3 2   +6 4   +2 2   +6 3   +5 4   +4 3   +3 5
————   ————   ————   ————   ————   ————   ————
 5 5    7 7    4 8    7 7    8 8    9 7    8 8
```

F

```
 2 3    6 2    4 6    4 5    8 1    2 3    4 4
+4 3   +1 5   +2 0   +3 2   +1 7   +6 5   +5 4
————   ————   ————   ————   ————   ————   ————
 6 6    7 7    6 6    7 7    9 8    8 8    9 8
```

G

```
 1 1    2 2    1 2    3 2    2 0     2     3
 2 1    2 3    2 1    3 0    1 2    3 2    2 0
 2 2    1 1    3 5    2 1    5 6    4 1    6 4
————   ————   ————   ————   ————   ————   ————
 5 4    5 6    6 8    8 3    8 8    7 5    8 7
```

H

```
  1    1 3      6    1 1    5 2    7 1    5 3
 5 3    3 4    2 0    2 2    1 4    1 7    1 5
 1 3    1 2    5 2    3 4    2 2    1 0    2 0
————   ————   ————   ————   ————   ————   ————
 6 7    5 9    7 8    6 7    8 8    9 8    8 8
```

I

```
  3    6 2      5    2 4     2      1     3
 2 1    1 2    4 0    1 4    7 4    8 5    6 4
 4 2    1 3    3 2    5 0    2 3    1 3    3 2
————   ————   ————   ————   ————   ————   ————
 6 6    8 7    7 7    8 8    9 9    9 9    9 9
```

Introduction of two columns and three rows, but no carrying.

4

ADDITION TABLE: 2
Work across the page

Time for Table
6 minutes.

Add (+):

A	$9+1=10$	$7+3=10$	$1+9=10$	$8+2=10$	$2+8=10$
B	$6+4=10$	$4+6=10$	$5+5=10$	$3+7=10$	$9+2=11$
C	$9+3=12$	$2+9=11$	$7+4=11$	$6+5=11$	$4+7=11$
D	$6+6=12$	$9+3=12$	$5+6=11$	$8+3=11$	$8+4=12$
E	$3+8=11$	$4+8=12$	$7+5=12$	$9+4=13$	$8+5=13$
F	$5+7=12$	$3+9=12$	$4+9=13$	$7+6=13$	$6+7=13$
G	$9+5=14$	$5+9=14$	$5+8=13$	$6+8=14$	$8+6=14$
H	$9+6=15$	$6+9=15$	$7+7=14$	$8+7=15$	$8+8=16$
I	$7+8=15$	$7+9=16$	$8+9=17$	$9+7=16$	$9+9=18$

Add (+):

A	15 +14 29	16 +13 29	22 +17 39	2 +19 21	5 +16 21	6 +15 21	6 +16 22
B	3 +18 21	8 +13 21	4 +17 21	4 +18 22	4 +16 20	3 +17 20	6 +14 20
C	5 +15 20	6 +24 30	9 +22 31	3 +28 31	5 +17 22	7 +23 30	8 +23 31
D	7 +14 21	8 +12 20	6 +27 33	7 +25 32	1 +39 40	3 +49 52	5 +39 44
E	2 +19 21	5 +37 42	4 +28 32	3 +29 32	4 +39 43	5 +48 53	6 +47 53

Completing the first group of addition combinations to 9+9 (maximum for two-row addition).   Introduction of carrying, but only tens and units in answers.

Add (+):

A	11 +19 — 30	12 +18 — 30	18 +12 — 30	5 +15 — 20	9 +11 — 20	13 +17 — 30	5 +27 — 32
B	14 +26 — 40	17 +23 — 40	26 +14 — 40	24 +15 — 39	13 +36 — 49	6 +45 — 51	3 +57 — 60
C	29 +22 — 51	23 +18 — 41	34 +18 — 52	38 +13 — 51	49 +13 — 62	37 +24 — 61	26 +35 — 61
D	12 +49 — 61	13 +59 — 72	34 +27 — 61	46 +16 — 62	47 +27 — 74	15 +46 — 61	28 +48 — 76
E	25 +37 — 62	35 +18 — 53	46 +17 — 63	27 +35 — 62	38 +24 — 62	44 +19 — 63	34 +37 — 71
F	15 +49 — 64	29 +44 — 73	37 +36 — 73	36 +38 — 74	37 +48 — 85	36 +49 — 85	28 +57 — 85
G	27 +49 — 76	48 +25 — 73	39 +45 — 84	48 +36 — 84	38 +49 — 87	29 +56 — 85	37 +46 — 83
H	18 +58 — 76	58 +17 — 75	29 +57 — 86	59 +28 — 87	49 +39 — 88	48 +49 — 97	45 +49 — 94
I	12 12 37 — 61	13 12 26 — 51	12 21 38 — 71	24 13 26 — 63	22 23 16 — 61	21 14 35 — 70	13 25 24 — 62

More difficult examples, with noughts in the answers of the first row.

6

Add (+):

A

12	11	10	12	11	23	14
22	10	34	13	12	22	30
15	28	17	15	27	15	16
49	**49**	**61**	**40**	**50**	**60**	**60**

B

15	15	25	3	3	7	6
12	10	20	26	17	42	30
14	34	35	31	41	12	34
41	**59**	**80**	**60**	**61**	**61**	**70**

C

6	15	14	20	6	50	40
43	4	6	6	10	8	5
33	14	42	57	74	28	44
82	**33**	**62**	**83**	**90**	**86**	**89**

D

12	8	9	9	7	4	6
20	10	30	21	30	10	55
29	23	12	33	26	49	10
61	**41**	**51**	**63**	**63**	**63**	**71**

E

5	16	18	28	17	19	25
20	13	30	14	30	2	30
28	5	5	30	7	33	7
53	**34**	**53**	**72**	**54**	**54**	**62**

F

17	19	28	15	29	8	5
30	24	26	9	5	20	35
28	20	30	40	30	47	40
75	**63**	**84**	**64**	**64**	**75**	**80**

G

18	26	19	29	37	28	36
37	29	6	50	9	4	34
21	30	50	7	30	43	20
76	**85**	**75**	**86**	**76**	**75**	**90**

H

24	16	27	35	28	47	39
33	34	7	40	50	35	47
20	4	51	9	7	4	12
77	**54**	**85**	**84**	**85**	**86**	**98**

More difficult examples, including noughts and omissions, but still only tens and units in answers.

Add (+):

7

A

22	34	21	38	40	50	70
+38	+56	+91	+91	+80	+66	+45
60	90	112	129	120	116	115

B

60	86	44	74	87	93	78
+45	+22	+60	+33	+32	+51	+61
105	108	104	107	119	144	139

C

91	80	13	36	50	20	60
+35	+40	+96	+70	+50	+80	+40
126	120	109	106	100	100	100

D

20	10	25	30	3	4	42
17	9	13	22	30	40	23
35	64	75	49	78	67	36
72	83	113	101	111	111	101

E

7	4	10	15	20	38	72
93	40	5	80	76	60	16
13	56	86	5	4	2	12
113	100	101	100	100	100	100

F

10	80	69	76	79	69	68
38	7	31	22	1	31	23
56	67	35	47	86	47	65
104	154	135	145	166	147	156

G

23	64	62	75	56	87	96
4	22	10	83	1	9	4
74	53	79	6	87	80	85
101	139	151	164	144	176	185

H

46	5	64	75	58	88	76
10	83	77	40	67	6	9
56	85	12	39	21	73	80
112	173	153	154	146	167	165

Rows **A–C** introduce examples having hundreds, tens and units in the answers, including noughts in the tens and units.

ADDITION WITH WORDS (1)

Write answers only

1	3+2.	5		**2**	3 plus 2.	5
3	4 plus 0.	4		**4**	7 plus 4.	11
5	6 plus 7.	13		**6**	8 plus 3.	11
7	Add 4 to 6.	10		**8**	Add 5 to 7.	12
9	Add 9 to 3.	12		**10**	Add 4 to 8.	12
11	Add five to four.	9		**12**	Add three to six.	9
13	To 6 add 5.	11		**14**	To 7 add 7.	14
15	Total 7 and 3.	10		**16**	Total 2 and 9.	11
17	Total 3 and 8.	11		**18**	Total 8 and 5.	13
19	Total 3, 4 and 2.	9		**20**	Total 5, 3 and 2	10
21	Six plus six.	12		**22**	Nine plus four.	13
23	Seven plus six.	13		**24**	Five plus nine.	14
25	Add five to eight.	13		**26**	Add seven to eight.	15
27	Add eight and eight.	16		**28**	To seven add nine.	16
29	Total nine and eight.	17		**30**	Total nine and nine.	18
31	Total six, three and five.	14		**32**	Total five, three and six.	14
33	Total one, four and nine.	14		**34**	Total six, three and nine.	18

Introduces the terms "plus, add, total", both with figures and words.

1 To 23 add 45.   68

2 Add 27 and 62.   89

3 What is 36 plus 42?   78

4 What is 35 plus 44?   79

5 Find the total of twenty and forty-six.   66

6 Find the total of twenty and fifty-four.   74

7 What is the total of fifty-one and sixty-nine?   120

8 What is the total of forty-eight and seventy-two?   120

9 What is thirty-seven plus eighty-eight?   125

10 What is twenty-six plus eighty-nine?   115

11 Find the total of thirty, twenty-one and forty-nine.   100

12 What is the total of 17, 40 and 36?   93

13 What is the total of nineteen, thirty and fifty-seven?   106

14 What is the total of eighteen, forty and forty-nine?   107

15 Find the total of twenty-five, forty and thirty-six.   101

16 Find the total of twenty-six, thirty-seven and forty-two.   105

17 What is seventy-one plus eighty-nine?   160

18 What is eighty-nine plus eighty-one?   170

19 Is sixty-five plus fifty-six greater than one hundred and forty?   No

20 Is seventy-four plus forty-seven greater than one hundred and fifty?   No

21 At darts Tom scored nineteen, eleven and sixty. What was the total?   90

22 Tina has 38 red marbles 40 blue and forty-seven green ones. What is the total?   125 marbles

If the teacher wishes these sums can be used as two separate groups, odd and even, both groups covering the same ground.

ADDITION TABLE: 3
Work across the page

Time for Table 6 minutes.

Add (+):

A	$10+1=11$	$10+0=10$	$11+1=12$	$10+2=12$	$12+1=13$
B	$11+2=13$	$10+3=13$	$10+4=14$	$13+1=14$	$14+1=15$
C	$11+3=14$	$12+2=14$	$12+3=15$	$15+1=16$	$16+1=17$
D	$15+0=15$	$10+5=15$	$11+5=16$	$10+6=16$	$17+1=18$
E	$11+4=15$	$12+4=16$	$14+0=14$	$11+6=17$	$10+7=17$
F	$11+7=18$	$12+5=17$	$13+2=15$	$13+3=16$	$10+8=18$
G	$11+8=19$	$18+1=19$	$12+6=18$	$14+2=16$	$15+2=17$
H	$12+7=19$	$12+8=20$	$10+9=19$	$11+9=20$	$12+9=21$
I	$13+4=17$	$14+4=18$	$14+3=17$	$13+5=18$	$15+3=18$

Add (+):

A
11	12	21	11	22	23	4
11	24	15	34	13	25	40
29	17	46	26	37	35	46
51	53	82	71	72	83	90

B
11	22	23	13	24	35	26
33	16	34	22	6	9	57
18	26	8	9	44	41	3
62	64	65	44	74	85	86

C
23	23	44	53	30	25	64
42	60	24	30	93	42	40
54	46	91	85	24	80	75
119	129	159	168	147	147	179

D
33	61	21	14	22	31	23
54	55	67	43	75	68	56
44	37	49	87	78	69	88
131	153	137	144	175	168	167

Introduces the easiest of the second group of addition combinations.

Add (+):

A	41 10 93	53 29 80	24 75 52	63 40 77	16 40 90	12 70 87	42 70 48
	144	162	151	180	146	169	160

B	54 45 70	12 71 86	13 76 93	41 50 98	47 50 75	46 67 60	85 80 16
	169	169	182	189	172	173	181

C	79 52 58	59 69 51	38 72 79	37 54 68	28 58 99	14 93 89	58 7 63
	189	179	189	159	185	196	128

D	65 4 88	45 54 9	61 35 9	73 5 28	39 68 82	4 87 17	59 48 4
	157	108	105	106	189	108	111

E	26 76 6	18 68 34	58 39 3	49 98 3	49 47 4	12 88 57	33 9 65
	108	120	100	150	100	157	107

F	35 74 69	81 59 60	43 86 49	84 96 28	19 80 79	89 77 35	97 56 56
	178	200	178	208	178	201	209

G	88 78 24	8 99 93	79 52 39	99 68 33	67 55 56	49 43 59	92 98 26
	190	200	170	200	178	151	216

H	64 6 95	81 97 19	39 8 84	99 20 99	84 6 98	98 9 93	99 23 89
	165	197	131	218	188	200	211

Completes practice with combinations from Table 3, including all previous types of difficulty.   Extend notation to 1,000.

12

ADDITION TABLE: 4
Work across the page

Time for Table
5 minutes.

Add (+):

A	13+7= 20	17+2= 19	16+2= 18	18+2= 20	16+3= 19
B	15+4= 19	14+5= 19	13+8= 21	18+3= 21	14+6= 20
C	17+3= 20	16+4= 20	13+9= 22	15+5= 20	15+6= 21
D	14+7= 21	17+4= 21	18+4= 22	14+8= 22	14+9= 23
E	15+7= 22	17+5= 22	15+8= 23	18+5= 23	16+5= 21
F	16+6= 22	17+6= 23	16+7= 23	18+6= 24	16+8= 24
G	17+0= 17	15+9= 24	16+9= 25	17+7= 24	17+8= 25
H	18+7= 25	17+9= 26	18+8= 26	18+9= 27	17+9= 26

Add (+):

A	27 15 37 **79**	7 56 47 **110**	54 77 69 **200**	42 68 98 **208**	8 42 99 **149**	35 86 98 **219**	28 97 56 **181**
B	52 69 79 **200**	26 76 79 **181**	46 65 79 **190**	23 78 89 **190**	53 48 98 **199**	54 54 99 **207**	37 78 76 **191**
C	44 48 79 **171**	46 54 89 **189**	37 56 97 **190**	58 75 78 **211**	69 86 67 **222**	58 85 79 **222**	45 79 85 **209**
D	43 99 49 **191**	35 99 67 **201**	57 98 55 **210**	46 89 74 **209**	89 95 38 **222**	47 79 96 **222**	66 78 59 **203**

Completes the combinations for three-row addition (max. 18+9).

Add (+):

A						
46	57	127	204	26	313	112
96	88	136	107	209	45	407
79	89	219	388	359	539	179
221	234	482	699	594	897	698

B						
207	394	269	224	143	184	45
156	105	386	168	137	167	256
358	278	187	478	599	367	698
721	777	842	870	879	718	999

C						
174	267	447	145	279	69	423
453	355	375	584	132	444	98
59	78	69	78	488	378	279
686	700	891	807	899	891	800

D						
352	474	535	296	238	452	23
69	69	77	120	80	69	388
389	358	188	384	582	379	289
810	901	800	800	900	900	700

E						
476	698	255	487	289	387	279
66	53	87	98	86	398	598
58	49	379	148	349	69	78
600	800	721	733	724	854	955

F						
589	293	99	699	784	66	118
99	67	554	76	60	497	90
78	339	68	58	56	58	702
766	699	721	833	900	621	910

G						
89	71	98	79	463	378	597
540	684	340	588	499	266	368
504	404	706	560	369	489	479
1133	1159	1144	1227	1331	1133	1444

H						
580	368	579	698	854	479	658
176	477	98	639	979	908	99
68	199	378	708	799	679	876
824	1044	1055	2045	2632	2066	1633

Introduces three-column addition, restricting answers to hundreds, tens and units as far as row F, but having thousands in the answers in rows G and H.

14

ADDITION WITH WORDS (3)

Write answers only

1 Nine plus five. 14
2 The total of 6 and 7. 13

3 The sum of 8 and 5. 13
4 Increase 5 by 3. 8

5 Increase 9 by 7. 16
6 The total of 8 and 6. 14

7 Increase 10 by 3. 13
8 The sum of 10 and 7. 17

9 Increase 14 by 6. 20
10 Increase 13 by 7. 20

11 Fifteen plus eight. 23
12 Sixteen plus five. 21

13 Fifteen plus nine. 24
14 The sum of 17 plus six. 23

15 Increase 18 by 9. 27
16 Add 8 plus 6 plus 7. 21

Work out on paper

17 What is the total of forty-four and seventy? 114
18 Find the sum of 67 and 76. 143

19 Increase thirty-six by eighty-four. 120
20 What is four-hundred-and-seven increased by sixty-nine? 476

21 Find the total of ninety-eight, seventy-six and fifty-eight. 232
22 Increase three-hundred-and-eight by ninety-seven. 405

23 What is the sum of twenty-three, forty and seventy-seven? 140
24 Find the total of ninety-three, seven and thirty-nine. 139

25 What is the total when 467 is increased by 59? 526
26 Add fifty-seven to the sum of two-hundred-and-sixty-three and four-hundred-and-eight. 728

Revision of previous terms with the addition of "the sum of" and "increase by".

15

ADDITION TABLE: 5

Work across the page

Time for Table
5 minutes.

Add (+):

A	19+1=20	19+0=19	20+1=21	19+2=21	21+1=22
B	20+2=22	19+3=22	22+1=23	21+2=23	20+3=23
C	19+4=23	23+1=24	23+3=26	21+3=24	20+4=24
D	19+5=24	21+4=25	22+2=24	22+3=25	20+5=25
E	22+4=26	19+6=25	20+6=26	21+5=26	24+1=25
F	23+2=25	19+7=26	19+8=27	20+7=27	21+6=27
G	24+0=24	24+2=26	25+0=25	25+1=26	24+3=27
H	23+4=27	19+9=28	20+8=28	20+9=29	22+5=27
I	19+0=19	21+7=28	21+8=29	22+6=28	22+7=29

Add (+):

A	176 588 358 **1122**	768 886 679 **2333**	956 698 800 **2454**	248 907 399 **1554**	598 69 788 **1455**	364 900 805 **2069**	246 75 909 **1230**
B	124 233 115 625 **1097**	231 106 412 504 **1253**	400 251 130 219 **1000**	352 375 284 308 **1319**	435 464 943 375 **2217**	265 373 97 508 **1243**	354 478 807 693 **2332**
C	202 734 686 855 **2477**	342 685 759 486 **2272**	465 256 887 549 **2157**	375 136 908 697 **2116**	489 705 389 990 **2573**	378 687 450 879 **2394**	508 399 776 588 **2271**
D	397 405 284 608 **1694**	279 686 53 238 **1256**	58 30 909 409 **1406**	419 283 56 248 **1006**	231 395 786 409 **1821**	212 745 376 888 **2221**	373 547 89 675 **1684**

Introduces the third group of addition combinations and four-row addition. Extend
notation to ten-thousand.

Add (+):

A	212	119	313	511	734	413
	567	400	694	43	480	256
	658	589	507	349	578	879
	896	779	899	97	208	797
	2333	**1887**	**2413**	**1000**	**2000**	**2345**

B	465	145	261	42	329	532
	643	646	605	795	500	678
	578	477	697	68	799	697
	768	897	999	956	589	759
	2454	**2165**	**2562**	**1861**	**2217**	**2666**

C	177	63	558	1040	1764	2653
	324	697	41	2607	2055	1097
	577	48	89	1098	2979	3804
	989	769	689	3899	1889	1078
	2067	**1577**	**1377**	**8644**	**8687**	**8632**

D	1898	1421	2324	1536	3114	5232
	2905	2308	1643	3053	659	698
	2587	1897	4788	968	3875	9075
	1598	3699	1579	2988	4787	856
	8988	**9325**	**10334**	**8545**	**12435**	**15861**

ADDITION TABLE: 6

Work across the page

Time for Table 5 minutes.

Add (+):

A	$3+5=8$	$13+5=18$	$23+5=28$	$20+9=29$	$25+2=27$
B	$2+8=10$	$12+8=20$	$22+8=30$	$26+1=27$	$25+3=28$
C	$3+7=10$	$13+7=20$	$23+7=30$	$26+2=28$	$27+3=30$
D	$8+3=11$	$18+3=21$	$28+3=31$	$24+4=28$	$21+9=30$
E	$4+7=11$	$14+7=21$	$24+7=31$	$23+8=31$	$27+1=28$
F	$25+4=29$	$24+5=29$	$27+2=29$	$26+3=29$	$22+9=31$
G	$25+5=30$	$24+7=31$	$27+4=31$	$26+5=31$	$25+6=31$
H	$25+7=32$	$26+6=32$	$27+6=33$	$24+8=32$	$23+9=32$
I	$26+7=33$	$25+8=33$	$27+7=34$	$24+9=33$	$26+8=34$

Introduces four-column addition and the final Addition Table. Notice revision of adding in tens in the first three examples in rows A–E of this Table.

Add (+):

A

115	241	596	768	587	476
476	357	378	307	96	586
388	488	456	97	778	979
689	599	769	858	689	78
1668	1685	2199	2030	2150	2119

B

895	546	69	568	797	683
68	99	560	89	99	79
989	377	898	697	659	88
307	579	678	806	608	969
2259	1601	2205	2160	2163	1819

C

1796	1465	786	5786	6785	7436
1984	3989	5496	798	799	798
2509	2796	5779	6969	5948	867
3879	5708	6908	5258	7478	5989
10168	13958	18969	18811	21010	15090

D

153	2875	6874	4756	6497	7586
342	384	4596	5697	678	4899
265	6459	9087	769	986	60
206	696	959	884	7569	589
374	9508	968	6079	8005	809
1340	19922	22484	18185	23735	13943

E

3564	635	5946	5785	4567	6987
8360	7075	889	4668	8599	98
876	8964	5793	8697	9698	809
9758	689	927	849	6706	70
4096	6587	4698	1076	7859	956
26654	23950	18253	21075	37429	8920

F

5463	7809	657	498	3078	6789
87	697	6978	4069	879	5008
8000	9	69	97	90	87
99	698	697	786	908	9
688	87	85	9	8070	878
14337	9300	8486	5459	13025	12771

Completes addition of number.

CHECK YOUR SUBTRACTION

						Further Practice	
						Table	Pages

A

$$\begin{array}{r} 3 \\ -2 \\ \hline 1 \end{array} \qquad \begin{array}{r} 4 \\ -0 \\ \hline 4 \end{array} \qquad \begin{array}{r} 5 \\ -3 \\ \hline 2 \end{array} \qquad \begin{array}{r} 7 \\ -4 \\ \hline 3 \end{array} \qquad \begin{array}{r} 9 \\ -5 \\ \hline 4 \end{array}$$

Table 1 — Pages 19

B

$$\begin{array}{r} 85 \\ -32 \\ \hline 53 \end{array} \qquad \begin{array}{r} 76 \\ -50 \\ \hline 26 \end{array} \qquad \begin{array}{r} 80 \\ -50 \\ \hline 30 \end{array} \qquad \begin{array}{r} 37 \\ -33 \\ \hline 4 \end{array} \qquad \begin{array}{r} 89 \\ -87 \\ \hline 2 \end{array}$$

Table 1 — Pages 20

C

$$\begin{array}{r} 10 \\ -7 \\ \hline 3 \end{array} \qquad \begin{array}{r} 20 \\ -9 \\ \hline 11 \end{array} \qquad \begin{array}{r} 70 \\ -13 \\ \hline 57 \end{array} \qquad \begin{array}{r} 51 \\ -14 \\ \hline 37 \end{array} \qquad \begin{array}{r} 92 \\ -25 \\ \hline 67 \end{array}$$

Table 2 — Pages 21 & 22

D

$$\begin{array}{r} 40 \\ -38 \\ \hline 2 \end{array} \qquad \begin{array}{r} 367 \\ -162 \\ \hline 205 \end{array} \qquad \begin{array}{r} 450 \\ -200 \\ \hline 250 \end{array} \qquad \begin{array}{r} 530 \\ -315 \\ \hline 215 \end{array} \qquad \begin{array}{r} 862 \\ -157 \\ \hline 705 \end{array}$$

Table 2 — Pages 23

E

$$\begin{array}{r} 416 \\ -296 \\ \hline 120 \end{array} \qquad \begin{array}{r} 505 \\ -210 \\ \hline 295 \end{array} \qquad \begin{array}{r} 623 \\ -583 \\ \hline 40 \end{array} \qquad \begin{array}{r} 800 \\ -206 \\ \hline 594 \end{array} \qquad \begin{array}{r} 721 \\ -66 \\ \hline 655 \end{array}$$

Table 2 — Pages 24 to 26

F

$$\begin{array}{r} 503 \\ -346 \\ \hline 157 \end{array} \qquad \begin{array}{r} 450 \\ -67 \\ \hline 383 \end{array} \qquad \begin{array}{r} 664 \\ -196 \\ \hline 468 \end{array} \qquad \begin{array}{r} 500 \\ -292 \\ \hline 208 \end{array} \qquad \begin{array}{r} 876 \\ -797 \\ \hline 79 \end{array}$$

Table 3 — Pages 27 & 28

G

$$\begin{array}{r} 6005 \\ -5096 \\ \hline 909 \end{array} \qquad \begin{array}{r} 7090 \\ -999 \\ \hline 6091 \end{array} \qquad \begin{array}{r} 32786 \\ -20690 \\ \hline 12096 \end{array} \qquad \begin{array}{r} 58991 \\ -1093 \\ \hline 57898 \end{array} \qquad \begin{array}{r} 80990 \\ -79997 \\ \hline 993 \end{array}$$

Table 3 — Pages 30

See pages iv and v for suggestions on how best to use this page. An alternative check page for subtraction is printed on page 73 of the Teacher's Edition.

SUBTRACTION TABLE: 1
Work across the page

Time for Table
4 minutes

19

Take away (−):

A	$2-1=1$	$1-0=1$	$0-0=0$	$1-1=0$	$2-0=2$
B	$2-2=0$	$3-1=2$	$3-0=3$	$3-2=1$	$3-3=0$
C	$4-1=3$	$4-3=1$	$4-4=0$	$4-0=4$	$4-2=2$
D	$5-1=4$	$5-4=1$	$5-5=0$	$6-6=0$	$6-0=6$
E	$5-0=5$	$6-1=5$	$6-5=1$	$7-0=7$	$7-7=0$
F	$7-1=6$	$7-6=1$	$8-8=0$	$8-0=8$	$8-1=7$
G	$8-7=1$	$9-0=9$	$9-9=0$	$9-1=8$	$9-8=1$

Take away (−):

A	$2-1=1$	$1-1=0$	$0-0=0$	$2-2=0$	$4-4=0$	$1-0=1$	$2-0=2$	$3-3=0$
B	$3-1=2$	$3-0=3$	$4-1=3$	$4-3=1$	$4-2=2$	$4-0=4$	$4-4=0$	$3-2=1$
C	$4-3=1$	$3-2=1$	$3-1=2$	$4-1=3$	$4-2=2$	$2-1=1$	$2-2=0$	$4-0=4$
D	$4-4=0$	$5-5=0$	$5-0=5$	$5-1=4$	$5-4=1$	$6-6=0$	$6-1=5$	$6-5=1$
E	$5-0=5$	$5-1=4$	$5-4=1$	$5-5=0$	$6-0=6$	$6-6=0$	$7-7=0$	$8-8=0$
F	$7-0=7$	$8-0=8$	$9-0=9$	$7-1=6$	$7-6=1$	$8-7=1$	$8-1=7$	$9-1=8$

Introduces practice of the combinations in an alternative vertical lay-out.

20 Take away (—):

A	6 −6 0	6 −0 6	6 −5 1	7 −6 1	8 −7 1	9 −1 8	9 −8 1
B	3 2 −2 1 1 1	2 3 −1 2 1 1	3 3 −1 0 2 3	4 2 −3 0 1 2	5 4 −1 1 4 3	4 5 −2 0 2 5	6 6 −1 0 5 6
C	7 5 −1 4 6 1	7 7 −6 0 1 7	7 4 −1 2 6 2	5 8 −4 0 1 8	6 5 −5 1 1 4	4 6 −3 5 1 1	8 7 −1 0 7 7
D	6 5 −1 0 5 5	4 4 −3 1 1 3	7 7 −6 1 1 6	8 9 −7 0 1 9	8 8 −1 0 7 8	9 9 −8 1 1 8	7 9 −6 8 1 1
E	3 9 −1 0 2 9	3 2 −2 2 1 0	6 3 −1 3 5 0	5 5 −4 5 1 0	5 4 −1 4 4 0	6 6 −1 6 5 0	8 5 −1 5 7 0
F	6 1 −5 1 1 0	4 6 −2 6 2 0	9 7 −1 7 8 0	9 8 −8 8 1 0	8 0 −7 0 1 0	7 9 −1 0 6 9	8 9 −7 9 1 0
G	4 3 −1 3 3 0	8 8 −1 8 7 0	2 4 −1 4 1 0	7 0 −0 0 7 0	5 9 −1 9 4 0	5 8 −4 8 1 0	9 0 −1 0 8 0
H	6 6 −5 6 1 0	2 3 −2 1 2	3 5 −3 4 1	4 4 −4 0 4	8 3 −8 0 3	5 2 −5 0 2	9 7 −9 6 1
I	7 7 −7 1 6	7 7 −7 6 1	8 8 −8 7 1	6 8 −6 1 7	7 9 −7 1 8	8 9 −8 8 1	9 9 −9 8 1

B—D No adding—two figure answers.
E—G No adding—same figures in units—two figure answers.
H—I No adding—same figures in tens.

SUBTRACTION TABLE: 2

Work across the page

Time for Table
5 minutes

Take away (—):

A	$5-2=3$	$5-3=2$	$6-2=4$	$6-4=2$	$6-3=3$
B	$7-5=2$	$7-2=5$	$7-3=4$	$7-4=3$	$8-2=6$
C	$9-2=7$	$9-7=2$	$8-6=2$	$8-3=5$	$8-5=3$
D	$8-4=4$	$9-6=3$	$9-3=6$	$9-5=4$	$9-4=5$
E	$10-9=1$	$10-1=9$	$10-8=2$	$11-9=2$	$10-2=8$
F	$11-2=9$	$11-3=8$	$10-3=7$	$10-7=3$	$11-7=4$
G	$10-6=4$	$10-4=6$	$11-4=7$	$11-6=5$	$10-5=5$
H	$11-5=6$	$11-8=3$	$12-3=9$	$12-9=3$	$12-6=6$

Take away (—):

A	$\begin{array}{r}59\\-30\\\hline29\end{array}$	$\begin{array}{r}58\\-20\\\hline38\end{array}$	$\begin{array}{r}76\\-32\\\hline44\end{array}$	$\begin{array}{r}65\\-32\\\hline33\end{array}$	$\begin{array}{r}78\\-23\\\hline55\end{array}$	$\begin{array}{r}60\\-40\\\hline20\end{array}$
B	$\begin{array}{r}10\\-1\\\hline9\end{array}$	$\begin{array}{r}10\\-9\\\hline1\end{array}$	$\begin{array}{r}10\\-2\\\hline8\end{array}$	$\begin{array}{r}10\\-3\\\hline7\end{array}$	$\begin{array}{r}10\\-7\\\hline3\end{array}$	$\begin{array}{r}10\\-8\\\hline2\end{array}$
C	$\begin{array}{r}10\\-4\\\hline6\end{array}$	$\begin{array}{r}10\\-6\\\hline4\end{array}$	$\begin{array}{r}10\\-3\\\hline7\end{array}$	$\begin{array}{r}10\\-2\\\hline8\end{array}$	$\begin{array}{r}10\\-8\\\hline2\end{array}$	$\begin{array}{r}10\\-7\\\hline3\end{array}$
D	$\begin{array}{r}10\\-6\\\hline4\end{array}$	$\begin{array}{r}20\\-6\\\hline14\end{array}$	$\begin{array}{r}20\\-1\\\hline19\end{array}$	$\begin{array}{r}20\\-9\\\hline11\end{array}$	$\begin{array}{r}20\\-5\\\hline15\end{array}$	$\begin{array}{r}30\\-3\\\hline27\end{array}$
E	$\begin{array}{r}20\\-1\\\hline19\end{array}$	$\begin{array}{r}30\\-2\\\hline28\end{array}$	$\begin{array}{r}40\\-5\\\hline35\end{array}$	$\begin{array}{r}40\\-6\\\hline34\end{array}$	$\begin{array}{r}50\\-7\\\hline43\end{array}$	$\begin{array}{r}70\\-9\\\hline61\end{array}$
F	$\begin{array}{r}10\\-9\\\hline1\end{array}$	$\begin{array}{r}40\\-4\\\hline36\end{array}$	$\begin{array}{r}50\\-8\\\hline42\end{array}$	$\begin{array}{r}60\\-6\\\hline54\end{array}$	$\begin{array}{r}60\\-3\\\hline57\end{array}$	$\begin{array}{r}80\\-5\\\hline75\end{array}$

Additional right-hand column:

A	$\begin{array}{r}95\\-75\\\hline20\end{array}$
B	$\begin{array}{r}10\\-5\\\hline5\end{array}$
C	$\begin{array}{r}10\\-5\\\hline5\end{array}$
D	$\begin{array}{r}30\\-4\\\hline26\end{array}$
E	$\begin{array}{r}80\\-8\\\hline72\end{array}$
F	$\begin{array}{r}90\\-7\\\hline83\end{array}$

D introduces "adding".

22

Take away (—):

A	10 − 2 8	20 − 1 19	30 − 0 30	50 − 0 50	70 − 8 62	90 − 6 84	90 − 7 83
B	60 − 3 57	30 −19 11	40 −19 21	60 −19 41	50 −19 31	80 −19 61	90 −19 71
C	70 −19 51	30 −11 19	50 −18 32	50 −12 38	60 −18 42	70 −13 57	80 −17 63
D	80 −14 66	90 −15 75	40 −29 11	40 −21 19	40 −25 15	50 −25 25	50 −29 21
E	60 −29 31	60 −32 28	70 −34 36	80 −42 38	70 −43 27	90 −26 64	80 −35 45
F	31 −19 12	31 −12 19	41 −12 29	71 −22 49	32 −19 13	52 −39 13	42 −23 19
G	51 −29 22	52 −36 16	71 −33 38	62 −29 33	81 −58 23	82 −43 39	92 −56 36
H	71 −44 27	61 −15 46	91 −37 54	92 −46 46	81 −66 15	72 −59 13	91 −68 23
I	80 −11 69	81 −17 64	72 −46 26	91 −15 76	82 −53 29	92 −36 56	92 −59 33

B introduces "adding" with two figures in subtrahend and answers.

Take away (−):

A

80	71	81	90	91	82	92
−15	−13	−46	−28	−47	−33	−66
65	58	35	62	44	49	26

B

30	50	60	40	51	31	62
−23	−47	−55	−36	−45	−23	−53
7	3	5	4	6	8	9

C

41	61	52	70	81	90	92
−34	−53	−46	−64	−76	−82	−89
7	8	6	6	5	8	3

D

550	340	406	507	610	830	704
−230	−120	−205	−103	−200	−500	−200
320	220	201	404	410	330	504

E

615	706	836	488	609	770	899
−210	−306	−306	−180	−402	−450	−353
405	400	530	308	207	320	546

F

801	673	690	708	890	898	909
−401	−373	−400	−206	−290	−668	−704
400	300	290	502	600	230	205

G

989	450	650	861	781	781	871
−239	−129	−431	−339	−347	−456	−458
750	321	219	522	434	325	413

H

391	932	741	621	752	971	891
−149	−323	−534	−315	−543	−763	−262
242	609	207	306	209	208	629

I

460	520	942	760	832	981	990
−113	−207	−633	−302	−209	−324	−427
347	313	309	458	623	657	563

B introduces single figure answers.
D introduces 3 Columns—no adding—but noughts in answers.
G introduces 3 Columns with adding in units column only.

24   **Take away (—):**

A

406	310	511	710	524	613	917
−192	−190	−181	−120	−233	−243	−353
214	120	330	590	291	370	564

B

841	819	809	906	817	729	808
−637	−146	−222	−236	−354	−494	−442
204	673	587	670	463	235	366

C

809	319	418	503	226	518	707
−655	−266	−375	−453	−195	−423	−694
154	53	43	50	31	95	13

D

410	310	212	604	417	809	728
−130	−230	−142	−564	−357	−779	−668
280	80	70	40	60	30	60

E

511	340	331	461	682	700	871
−461	−108	−207	−308	−603	−610	−802
50	232	124	153	79	90	69

F

400	500	401	612	502	600	701
−181	−271	−214	−386	−306	−204	−305
219	229	187	226	196	396	396

G

600	410	602	511	701	800	912
−309	− 53	− 49	− 77	− 58	− 17	− 83
291	357	553	434	643	783	829

H

700	512	811	607	111	101	802
−207	− 13	− 14	−527	− 43	− 26	−739
493	499	797	80	68	75	63

I

702	601	600	812	702	822	900
−306	−105	−580	−779	− 89	−703	−801
396	496	20	33	613	119	99

A introduces adding in tens column only.
C introduces 2 figure answers.
F introduces adding in both units and tens columns.

SUBTRACTION WITH WORDS (1)

Write answers only

1	From 7 take 3.	4	**2**	From 7 take 4.	3
3	From 9 take 1.	8	**4**	Take 0 from 9.	9
5	Take 3 from 8.	5	**6**	Take 6 from 8.	2
7	From 9 take 2.	7	**8**	Take 5 from 9.	4
9	Take 3 from 10.	7	**10**	From 9 take 6.	3
11	Take 7 from 10.	3	**12**	From 10 take 2.	8
13	From 10 take 6.	4	**14**	Take 4 from 10.	6
15	Subtract 5 from 8.	3	**16**	Subtract 2 from 7.	5
17	Subtract 4 from 9.	5	**18**	Subtract 7 from 9.	2
19	Take 2 from 11.	9	**20**	From 9 take 3.	6
21	Subtract 3 from 11.	8	**22**	Subtract 4 from 11.	7
23	From 11 take 5.	6	**24**	Take 3 from 12.	9
25	Subtract 6 from 11.	5	**26**	From 11 take 7.	4
27	Take 8 from 10.	2	**28**	Subtract 7 from 10.	3
29	From 11 take 8.	3	**30**	Take 6 from 12.	6
31	Subtract 9 from 10.	1	**32**	Subtract 8 from 11.	3
33	8 minus 4.	4	**34**	10 minus 3.	7
35	9 minus 9.	0	**36**	11 minus 11.	0
37	11 minus 9.	2	**38**	11 minus 0.	11
39	Subtract 9 from 12.	3	**40**	12 minus 9.	3

This page introduces terms "From—take—, Take—from—, Subtract, Minus".
The examples can be used in sequence, or as two columns, odds and evens, both being
of similar difficulty.

26

SUBTRACTION WITH WORDS (2)

Work out on paper

1 From 88 take 35. 53
2 From 77 take 43. 34

3 Take 26 from 96. 70
4 Take 34 from 94. 60

5 Subtract thirty-one from seventy. 39
6 Subtract forty-nine from eighty. 31

7 Sixty-two minus thirty-three. 29
8 Ninety-one minus fifty-six. 35

9 By how many is ninety greater than fifty-one? 39
10 By how many is 372 greater than 129? 243

11 By how many is 450 greater than 208? 242
12 By how many is 690 greater than 306? 384

13 Subtract one hundred and twenty from three hundred. 180
14 Subtract one hundred and thirty from four hundred. 270

15 How much less than 91 is 25? 66
16 How many less than 309 is 155? 154

17 How many less than 318 is 175? 143
18 Five hundred and ten minus seventy. 440

19 By how many is 146 less than 526? 380
20 By how many is 394 less than 629? 235

21 By how many is five hundred and eighty-two greater than five hundred and three? 79
22 By how many is eight hundred and six less than eight hundred and eighty? 74

Introduces the terms "how much greater than" and "how much less than".

SUBTRACTION TABLE: 3

Work across the page

Time for Table
5 minutes

Take away (−):

A	12−10=2	12− 4=8	13− 4=9	13− 9=4	14− 5=9
B	12− 5=7	13− 5=8	12− 7=5	13− 6=7	13− 7=6
C	12− 8=4	13− 8=5	14− 6=8	14− 8=6	14− 7=7
D	15− 6=9	15− 9=6	14− 9=5	15− 7=8	15− 8=7
E	16− 7=9	17− 8=9	10−10=0	11−10=1	13−10=3
F	16− 8=8	16−10=6	14−10=4	15−10=5	16− 9=7
G	17− 9=8	18−10=8	17−10=7	19−10=9	18− 9=9

Take away (−):

A	322−115=207	420−240=180	243−144=99	352−157=195	463−265=198	342−258=84	456−368=88
B	524−236=288	637−548=89	505−377=128	705−248=457	243−67=176	435−79=356	547−79=468
C	470−373=97	743−689=54	568−89=479	602−505=97	503−134=369	334−255=79	754−656=98
D	502−257=245	443−67=376	526−77=449	343−278=65	456−378=78	630−87=543	840−785=55
E	465−189=276	787−689=98	312−184=128	423−134=289	532−235=297	643−245=398	754−286=468
F	543−166=377	664−365=299	475−286=189	382−187=195	793−387=406	574−367=207	882−488=394

This page uses all previous steps to give practice on Table 3.

28 **Take away (—):**

A

413	324	433	745	654	566
−298	−198	−299	−498	−399	−298
115	126	134	247	255	268

B

595	637	412	523	233	444
−197	−498	−195	−294	− 95	− 95
398	139	217	229	138	349

C

452	372	763	482	672	793
−297	− 98	− 96	− 97	− 98	− 97
155	274	667	385	574	696

D

613	710	890	697	510	600
−399	−495	−299	−394	−299	−391
214	215	591	303	211	209

E

500	400	600	500	800	800
−299	−193	−494	−196	−498	−297
201	207	106	304	302	503

F

733	243	125	144	254	165
−395	− 96	− 96	− 99	−197	− 97
338	147	29	45	57	68

G

870	603	494	686	796	560
− 98	− 98	−398	−599	−397	−409
772	505	96	87	399	151

H

400	500	300	600	503	700
−309	−205	− 91	− 97	−107	− 93
91	295	209	503	396	607

I

205	734	190	596	706	845
−106	−697	− 99	−497	−698	−798
99	37	91	99	8	47

This page introduces nine in the tens column of the subtrahend.

Write answers only:

1 13 minus 6.   7

2 15 minus 7.   8

3 Reduce 13 by 5.   8

4 Reduce 15 by 8.   7

5 Reduce 17 by 10.   7

6 Reduce 14 by 9.   5

7 Subtract 8 from 16.   8

8 18 minus 10.   8

9 Find the difference be-
   tween 12 and 8.   4

10 Find the difference
    between 15 and 7.   8

11 Find the difference be-
    tween 9 and 16.   7

12 By how much is 19
    greater than 10?   9

Work out on paper:

13 Reduce eighty-three by
    forty-seven.   36

14 Subtract four-hundred-
    and-twenty from six-
    hundred.   180

15 By how much is six-
    hundred-and-six less than
    eight-hundred?   194

16 Find the difference be-
    tween 307 and 401   94

17 Find the difference be-
    tween seven-hundred-
    and-one and ninety-nine.   602

18 Reduce eight-hundred by
    five-hundred-and-ninety-
    nine.   201

19 Find the difference be-
    tween 703 and 900.   197

20 Reduce 7001 by 6009.   992

Introduces terms "reduce" and "find the difference".

30   Take away (−):

A

394	605	503	404	695
−196	−297	−198	− 98	− 98
198	308	305	306	597

B

6476	4527	3055	4706	3767
−3278	−1898	−1299	−1809	−1999
3198	2629	1756	2897	1768

C

5602	4384	6512	4432	5508
− 804	− 395	− 505	−3997	− 909
4798	3989	6007	435	4599

D

3393	3604	5003	7542	1043
− 595	−2976	− 957	−6668	− 978
2798	628	4046	874	65

E

1356	7000	5076	6043	8008
− 977	− 991	−1078	− 989	−7009
379	6009	3998	5054	999

F

1005	2006	4007	8000	1870
− 909	−1099	−3909	−7995	− 999
96	907	98	5	871

G

4132	35003	52324	62254
−2944	−24574	−18545	−19656
1188	10429	33779	42598

H

34303	74900	60105	84151
−16907	−29991	−50097	−74154
17396	44909	10008	9997

I

66566	18765	10087	90003
− 9968	− 9989	− 9089	−80906
56598	8776	998	9097

This page completes subtraction.

	CHECK YOUR MULTIPLICATION			Further Practice	
				Table	Pages

A
$$\begin{array}{r} 12 \\ \times\ 2 \\ \hline 24 \end{array}\qquad \begin{array}{r} 31 \\ \times\ 3 \\ \hline 93 \end{array}\qquad \begin{array}{r} 40 \\ \times\ 5 \\ \hline 200 \end{array}\qquad \begin{array}{r} 62 \\ \times\ 4 \\ \hline 248 \end{array}$$
  Table 1 — Pages 32

B
$$\begin{array}{r} 14 \\ \times\ 3 \\ \hline 42 \end{array}\qquad \begin{array}{r} 25 \\ \times\ 4 \\ \hline 100 \end{array}\qquad \begin{array}{r} 54 \\ \times\ 5 \\ \hline 270 \end{array}\qquad \begin{array}{r} 65 \\ \times\ 6 \\ \hline 390 \end{array}$$
  Table 1 — Pages 33 & 34

C
$$\begin{array}{r} 28 \\ \times\ 2 \\ \hline 56 \end{array}\qquad \begin{array}{r} 67 \\ \times\ 3 \\ \hline 201 \end{array}\qquad \begin{array}{r} 89 \\ \times\ 6 \\ \hline 534 \end{array}\qquad \begin{array}{r} 97 \\ \times\ 9 \\ \hline 873 \end{array}$$
  Table 2 — Pages 36 & 37

D
$$\begin{array}{r} 420 \\ \times\ 3 \\ \hline 1260 \end{array}\qquad \begin{array}{r} 215 \\ \times\ 4 \\ \hline 860 \end{array}\qquad \begin{array}{r} 240 \\ \times\ 5 \\ \hline 1200 \end{array}\qquad \begin{array}{r} 605 \\ \times\ 6 \\ \hline 3630 \end{array}$$
  Table 2 — Pages 38

E
$$\begin{array}{r} 306 \\ \times\ 5 \\ \hline 1530 \end{array}\qquad \begin{array}{r} 879 \\ \times\ 4 \\ \hline 3516 \end{array}\qquad \begin{array}{r} 709 \\ \times\ 7 \\ \hline 4963 \end{array}\qquad \begin{array}{r} 897 \\ \times\ 9 \\ \hline 8073 \end{array}$$
  Table 2 — Pages 39

F
$$\begin{array}{r} 43 \\ \times\ 10 \\ \hline 430 \end{array}\qquad \begin{array}{r} 156 \\ \times\ 11 \\ \hline 1716 \end{array}\qquad \begin{array}{r} 505 \\ \times\ 12 \\ \hline 6060 \end{array}\qquad \begin{array}{r} 678 \\ \times\ 12 \\ \hline 8136 \end{array}$$
  Table 3 — Pages 41 & 42

G
$$\begin{array}{r} 491 \\ \times\ 11 \\ \hline 5401 \end{array}\qquad \begin{array}{r} 699 \\ \times\ 11 \\ \hline 7689 \end{array}\qquad \begin{array}{r} 509 \\ \times\ 12 \\ \hline 6108 \end{array}\qquad \begin{array}{r} 789 \\ \times\ 12 \\ \hline 9468 \end{array}$$
  Table 3 — Pages 42G

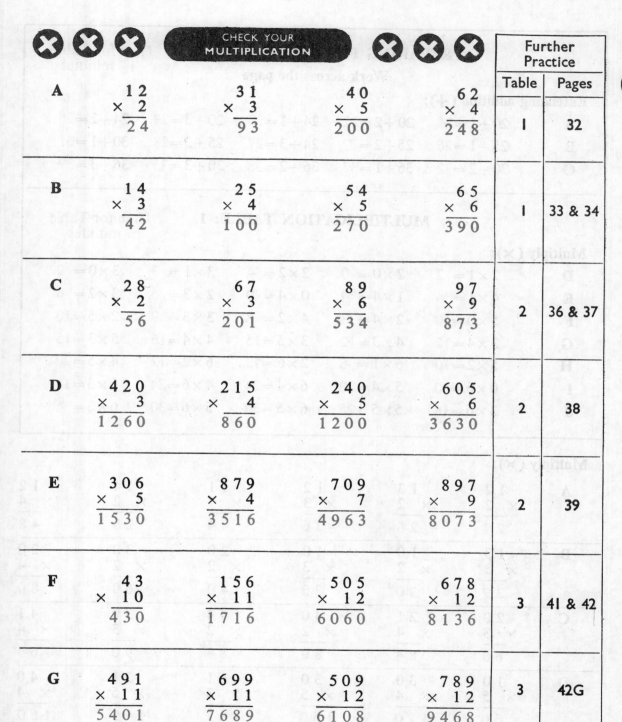

See pages iv and v for suggestions on how best to use this page.   An alternative check page for multiplication is printed on page 74 of the Teacher's Edition.

PREPARING FOR MULTIPLICATION
Time for Table 1½ minutes
Work across the page

Extending addition (+):

A	20+1=21	20+2=22	24+1=25	20+3=23	24+2=26
B	25+1=26	25+2=27	24+3=27	25+3=28	30+1=31
C	30+2=32	36+1=37	36+2=38	30+3=33	36+3=39

MULTIPLICATION TABLE: 1
Time for Table 3 minutes

Multiply (✗):

D	2×1= 2	2×0= 0	2×2= 4	3×1= 3	3×0= 0
E	4×1= 4	1×4= 4	0×4= 0	2×3= 6	3×2= 6
F	5×0= 0	2×4= 8	4×2= 8	3×3= 9	2×5=10
G	3×4=12	4×3=12	3×5=15	4×4=16	5×3=15
H	5×2=10	6×1= 6	2×6=12	6×2=12	4×5=20
I	0×6= 0	5×4=20	6×4=24	4×6=24	6×3=18
J	3×6=18	5×5=25	6×5=30	5×6=30	6×6=36

Multiply (✗):

A 12×2=24 13×2=26 12×3=36 11×4=44 14×2=28 12×4=48

B 13×3=39 10×2=20 10×3=30 20×2=40 30×2=60 20×4=80

C 20×3=60 21×4=84 40×2=80 44×2=88 30×3=90 41×4=164

D 10×5=50 30×4=120 30×5=150 61×3=183 31×5=155 40×4=160

First group of number combinations to 6×6, and extension of addition to 36+3 without carrying.

Multiply (✗):

A

31	60	32	51	50	42
× 4	× 2	× 3	× 2	× 3	× 4
1 2 4	1 2 0	9 6	1 0 2	1 5 0	1 6 8

B

32	30	40	50	54	51
× 4	× 4	× 5	× 4	× 2	× 3
1 2 8	1 2 0	2 0 0	2 0 0	1 0 8	1 5 3

C

41	43	53	62	60	63
× 5	× 3	× 3	× 3	× 4	× 3
2 0 5	1 2 9	1 5 9	1 8 6	2 4 0	1 8 9

D

51	52	62	50	61	20
× 4	× 4	× 4	× 5	× 4	× 6
2 0 4	2 0 8	2 4 8	2 5 0	2 4 4	1 2 0

E

21	30	51	41	60	50
× 6	× 6	× 5	× 6	× 5	× 6
1 2 6	1 8 0	2 5 5	2 4 6	3 0 0	3 0 0

F

13	14	16	13	13	14
× 3	× 3	× 2	× 4	× 6	× 4
3 9	4 2	3 2	5 2	7 8	5 6

G

15	16	15	15	12	14
× 3	× 3	× 2	× 4	× 5	× 5
4 5	4 8	3 0	6 0	6 0	7 0

H

13	12	15	16	14	15
× 5	× 6	× 5	× 4	× 6	× 6
6 5	7 2	7 5	6 4	8 4	9 0

I

22	26	36	23	25	26
× 2	× 2	× 2	× 4	× 3	× 4
4 4	5 2	7 2	9 2	7 5	1 0 4

F introduces carrying.

34   **Multiply (×):**

A
$$\begin{array}{r} 23 \\ \times\ 3 \\ \hline 69 \end{array}\qquad \begin{array}{r} 24 \\ \times\ 3 \\ \hline 72 \end{array}\qquad \begin{array}{r} 26 \\ \times\ 3 \\ \hline 78 \end{array}\qquad \begin{array}{r} 46 \\ \times\ 2 \\ \hline 92 \end{array}\qquad \begin{array}{r} 25 \\ \times\ 2 \\ \hline 50 \end{array}\qquad \begin{array}{r} 15 \\ \times\ 4 \\ \hline 60 \end{array}$$

B
$$\begin{array}{r} 35 \\ \times\ 2 \\ \hline 70 \end{array}\qquad \begin{array}{r} 45 \\ \times\ 2 \\ \hline 90 \end{array}\qquad \begin{array}{r} 35 \\ \times\ 3 \\ \hline 105 \end{array}\qquad \begin{array}{r} 25 \\ \times\ 4 \\ \hline 100 \end{array}\qquad \begin{array}{r} 22 \\ \times\ 5 \\ \hline 110 \end{array}\qquad \begin{array}{r} 24 \\ \times\ 5 \\ \hline 120 \end{array}$$

C
$$\begin{array}{r} 32 \\ \times\ 5 \\ \hline 160 \end{array}\qquad \begin{array}{r} 35 \\ \times\ 4 \\ \hline 140 \end{array}\qquad \begin{array}{r} 34 \\ \times\ 4 \\ \hline 136 \end{array}\qquad \begin{array}{r} 34 \\ \times\ 5 \\ \hline 170 \end{array}\qquad \begin{array}{r} 44 \\ \times\ 3 \\ \hline 132 \end{array}\qquad \begin{array}{r} 45 \\ \times\ 3 \\ \hline 135 \end{array}$$

D
$$\begin{array}{r} 45 \\ \times\ 4 \\ \hline 180 \end{array}\qquad \begin{array}{r} 25 \\ \times\ 5 \\ \hline 125 \end{array}\qquad \begin{array}{r} 55 \\ \times\ 2 \\ \hline 110 \end{array}\qquad \begin{array}{r} 44 \\ \times\ 4 \\ \hline 176 \end{array}\qquad \begin{array}{r} 56 \\ \times\ 2 \\ \hline 112 \end{array}\qquad \begin{array}{r} 22 \\ \times\ 6 \\ \hline 132 \end{array}$$

E
$$\begin{array}{r} 32 \\ \times\ 6 \\ \hline 192 \end{array}\qquad \begin{array}{r} 24 \\ \times\ 6 \\ \hline 144 \end{array}\qquad \begin{array}{r} 25 \\ \times\ 6 \\ \hline 150 \end{array}\qquad \begin{array}{r} 65 \\ \times\ 2 \\ \hline 130 \end{array}\qquad \begin{array}{r} 33 \\ \times\ 6 \\ \hline 198 \end{array}\qquad \begin{array}{r} 35 \\ \times\ 5 \\ \hline 175 \end{array}$$

F
$$\begin{array}{r} 46 \\ \times\ 3 \\ \hline 138 \end{array}\qquad \begin{array}{r} 26 \\ \times\ 6 \\ \hline 156 \end{array}\qquad \begin{array}{r} 36 \\ \times\ 4 \\ \hline 144 \end{array}\qquad \begin{array}{r} 43 \\ \times\ 5 \\ \hline 215 \end{array}\qquad \begin{array}{r} 54 \\ \times\ 4 \\ \hline 216 \end{array}\qquad \begin{array}{r} 44 \\ \times\ 5 \\ \hline 220 \end{array}$$

G
$$\begin{array}{r} 34 \\ \times\ 6 \\ \hline 204 \end{array}\qquad \begin{array}{r} 66 \\ \times\ 2 \\ \hline 132 \end{array}\qquad \begin{array}{r} 55 \\ \times\ 3 \\ \hline 165 \end{array}\qquad \begin{array}{r} 45 \\ \times\ 5 \\ \hline 225 \end{array}\qquad \begin{array}{r} 56 \\ \times\ 3 \\ \hline 168 \end{array}\qquad \begin{array}{r} 54 \\ \times\ 5 \\ \hline 270 \end{array}$$

H
$$\begin{array}{r} 56 \\ \times\ 4 \\ \hline 224 \end{array}\qquad \begin{array}{r} 35 \\ \times\ 6 \\ \hline 210 \end{array}\qquad \begin{array}{r} 42 \\ \times\ 6 \\ \hline 252 \end{array}\qquad \begin{array}{r} 64 \\ \times\ 3 \\ \hline 192 \end{array}\qquad \begin{array}{r} 65 \\ \times\ 4 \\ \hline 260 \end{array}\qquad \begin{array}{r} 66 \\ \times\ 4 \\ \hline 264 \end{array}$$

I
$$\begin{array}{r} 43 \\ \times\ 6 \\ \hline 258 \end{array}\qquad \begin{array}{r} 54 \\ \times\ 6 \\ \hline 324 \end{array}\qquad \begin{array}{r} 66 \\ \times\ 5 \\ \hline 330 \end{array}\qquad \begin{array}{r} 46 \\ \times\ 6 \\ \hline 276 \end{array}\qquad \begin{array}{r} 56 \\ \times\ 6 \\ \hline 336 \end{array}\qquad \begin{array}{r} 65 \\ \times\ 6 \\ \hline 390 \end{array}$$

More difficult examples giving practice in the number combinations in Table **1.**

MULTIPLICATION WITH WORDS (1)

Write answers only

1	3 times 2.	6	**2**	2 times 3.	6
3	2 times 4.	8	**4**	3 times 3.	9
5	Four times three.	12	**6**	Three times four.	12
7	Five times two.	10	**8**	Four times four.	16
9	Three fives.	15	**10**	Two sixes.	12
11	Six twos.	12	**12**	Five threes.	15
13	Three sixes.	18	**14**	Four fives.	20
15	Five times four.	20	**16**	Six times three.	18
17	Multiply 4 by 3.	12	**18**	Multiply 2 by 5.	10
19	Multiply 5 by 4.	20	**20**	Multiply 3 by 6.	18
21	5 multiplied by 5.	25	**22**	6 multiplied by 4.	24
23	4 multiplied by 6.	24	**24**	5 multiplied by 6.	30

Work out on paper

25	What number is 3 times 32?	96	**26**	Multiply twenty-six by five.	130
27	What number is four times fifty-two?	208	**28**	What number is forty-five times four?	180
29	Multiply thirty-six by five.	180	**30**	What is forty-four multiplied by five?	220
31	What is fifty-one multiplied by six?	306	**32**	What number is six times sixty-six?	396

Introduces the terms "times, multiply . . . by", and "multiplied by".

PREPARING FOR MULTIPLICATION
Time for Table $3\frac{1}{2}$ minutes

Work across the page

Extending addition (+):

A	21+3=24	27+2=29	27+4=31	28+3=31	27+5=32
B	32+8=40	25+6=31	27+7=34	28+5=33	36+5=41
C	40+7=47	42+4=46	45+3=48	36+7=43	28+8=36
D	45+5=50	48+3=51	49+2=51	42+8=50	48+5=53
E	49+6=55	45+8=53	54+3=57	56+5=61	48+7=55
F	54+5=59	56+7=63	63+4=67	54+8=62	64+5=69
G	72+4=76	63+6=69	64+7=71	63+8=71	72+8=80

MULTIPLICATION TABLE: 2
Time for Table $3\frac{1}{2}$ minutes

Multiply (×):

H	8×1= 8	9×0= 0	2×7=14	7×2=14	2×8=16
I	3×7=21	8×2=16	3×8=24	8×3=24	7×3=21
J	2×9=18	9×2=18	4×7=28	7×4=28	7×5=35
K	8×4=32	4×8=32	5×7=35	6×7=42	7×6=42
L	3×9=27	9×3=27	4×9=36	5×8=40	9×4=36
M	8×5=40	6×8=48	8×6=48	5×9=45	9×5=45
N	6×9=54	9×6=54	7×7=49	8×8=64	7×8=56
O	8×7=56	7×9=63	9×7=63	9×8=72	9×9=81

Multiply (×):

A	38 × 2 76	32 × 7 224	29 × 3 87	23 × 8 184	67 × 3 201	24 × 9 216
B	67 × 4 268	85 × 4 340	45 × 8 360	68 × 3 204	47 × 5 235	56 × 7 392

Practice on Table 2.

Multiply (✗):

✗

A

```
   5 6        7 5        7 6        6 7        7 7        9 5
 ×   6      ×   4      ×   5      ×   6      ×   2      ×   4
 ─────      ─────      ─────      ─────      ─────      ─────
 3 3 6      3 0 0      3 8 0      4 0 2      1 5 4      3 8 0
```

B

```
   2 8        2 4        6 8        4 9        6 5        7 3
 ×   7      ×   8      ×   5      ×   5      ×   8      ×   8
 ─────      ─────      ─────      ─────      ─────      ─────
 1 9 6      1 9 2      3 4 0      2 4 5      5 2 0      5 8 4
```

C

```
   7 9        7 3        5 7        8 9        7 6        7 5
 ×   3      ×   9      ×   7      ×   4      ×   5      ×   6
 ─────      ─────      ─────      ─────      ─────      ─────
 2 3 7      6 5 7      3 9 9      3 5 6      3 8 0      4 5 0
```

D

```
   8 9        7 9        8 9        5 6        8 4        6 9
 ×   3      ×   5      ×   5      ×   9      ×   7      ×   6
 ─────      ─────      ─────      ─────      ─────      ─────
 2 6 7      3 9 5      4 4 5      5 0 4      5 8 8      4 1 4
```

E

```
   6 9        8 8        9 6        8 5        9 9        6 2
 ×   7      ×   5      ×   5      ×   6      ×   4      ×   9
 ─────      ─────      ─────      ─────      ─────      ─────
 4 8 3      4 4 0      4 8 0      5 1 0      3 9 6      5 5 8
```

F

```
   7 5        7 8        4 9        7 8        8 2        7 5
 ×   7      ×   6      ×   7      ×   7      ×   8      ×   8
 ─────      ─────      ─────      ─────      ─────      ─────
 5 2 5      4 6 8      3 4 3      5 4 6      6 5 6      6 0 0
```

G

```
   7 9        9 6        8 3        7 4        7 6        8 6
 ×   6      ×   7      ×   8      ×   9      ×   8      ×   8
 ─────      ─────      ─────      ─────      ─────      ─────
 4 7 4      6 7 2      6 6 4      6 6 6      6 0 8      6 8 8
```

H

```
   8 9        7 5        9 4        6 9        7 7        8 9
 ×   6      ×   9      ×   8      ×   8      ×   8      ×   7
 ─────      ─────      ─────      ─────      ─────      ─────
 5 3 4      6 7 5      7 5 2      5 5 2      6 1 6      6 2 3
```

I

```
   6 8        9 5        9 4        8 5        8 9        9 6
 ×   9      ×   8      ×   9      ×   9      ×   8      ×   9
 ─────      ─────      ─────      ─────      ─────      ─────
 6 1 2      7 6 0      8 4 6      7 6 5      7 1 2      8 6 4
```

Further practice on Table 2.

38   **Multiply (×):**

A

224	302	203	320	301	502
× 2	× 3	× 4	× 4	× 5	× 4
448	906	812	1280	1505	2008

B

310	420	201	401	500	501
× 4	× 3	× 5	× 5	× 4	× 6
1240	1260	1005	2005	2000	3006

C

113	123	114	125	214	213
× 4	× 4	× 3	× 3	× 4	× 5
452	492	342	375	856	1065

D

212	126	315	214	325	213
× 6	× 2	× 2	× 5	× 4	× 6
1272	252	630	1070	1300	1278

E

325	324	314	216	315	416
× 3	× 4	× 5	× 5	× 6	× 6
975	1296	1570	1080	1890	2496

F

141	231	131	262	364	242
× 3	× 4	× 5	× 2	× 2	× 3
423	924	655	524	728	726

G

253	360	240	260	221	320
× 3	× 3	× 4	× 4	× 5	× 5
759	1080	960	1040	1105	1600

H

454	340	450	451	560	550
× 2	× 5	× 5	× 6	× 6	× 6
908	1700	2250	2706	3360	3300

I

115	203	304	305	404	506
× 6	× 7	× 6	× 4	× 5	× 5
690	1421	1824	1220	2020	2530

A—B   No carrying.
C—E   Carrying in units only, no noughts in tens.
F—H   Carrying in tens only.
I   Carrying in units only, noughts in tens.

Multiply (✕):

A

| 204 ✕ 7 = 1428 | 304 ✕ 8 = 2432 | 506 ✕ 7 = 3542 | 406 ✕ 8 = 3248 | 705 ✕ 6 = 4230 | 307 ✕ 9 = 2763 |

B

| 706 ✕ 5 = 3530 | 806 ✕ 5 = 4030 | 505 ✕ 8 = 4040 | 608 ✕ 7 = 4256 | 706 ✕ 8 = 5648 | 508 ✕ 8 = 4064 |

C

| 366 ✕ 2 = 732 | 457 ✕ 3 = 1371 | 478 ✕ 2 = 956 | 389 ✕ 2 = 778 | 367 ✕ 3 = 1101 | 479 ✕ 3 = 1437 |

D

| 589 ✕ 2 = 1178 | 378 ✕ 4 = 1512 | 789 ✕ 4 = 3156 | 608 ✕ 5 = 3040 | 566 ✕ 5 = 2830 | 798 ✕ 5 = 3990 |

E

| 485 ✕ 6 = 2910 | 478 ✕ 6 = 2868 | 348 ✕ 7 = 2436 | 589 ✕ 6 = 3534 | 469 ✕ 7 = 3283 | 257 ✕ 9 = 2313 |

F

| 908 ✕ 5 = 4540 | 709 ✕ 6 = 4254 | 750 ✕ 7 = 5250 | 630 ✕ 8 = 5040 | 820 ✕ 8 = 6560 | 432 ✕ 9 = 3888 |

G

| 627 ✕ 7 = 4389 | 789 ✕ 3 = 2367 | 753 ✕ 7 = 5271 | 790 ✕ 7 = 5530 | 427 ✕ 8 = 3416 | 548 ✕ 9 = 4932 |

H

| 786 ✕ 7 = 5502 | 897 ✕ 6 = 5382 | 680 ✕ 9 = 6120 | 960 ✕ 9 = 8640 | 895 ✕ 7 = 6265 | 839 ✕ 8 = 6712 |

I

| 898 ✕ 7 = 6286 | 687 ✕ 9 = 6183 | 897 ✕ 8 = 7176 | 899 ✕ 9 = 8091 | 989 ✕ 8 = 7912 | 997 ✕ 9 = 8973 |

C introduces carrying in units and tens.

39

MULTIPLICATION WITH WORDS (2)

40

Write answers only

1 Eight times three. **24**   2 Three times eight. **24**

3 Three sevens. **21**   4 Three nines. **27**

5 Multiply 4 by 8. **32**   6 Multiply 5 by 7. **35**

7 How many is 7×6? **42**   8 How many is 9×4? **36**

9 How many is 8×5? **40**   10 How many is 7×7? **49**

11 Multiply 5×9. **45**   12 Multiply 8 by 7. **56**

13 9 multiplied by 6. **54**   14 8 multiplied by 8. **64**

15 How many is 7 times 9? **63**   16 How many is 9 times 8? **72**

17 8 Multiplied by 9. **72**   18 Multiply 9 by 9. **81**

Work these sums in your book:

19 How many is two times seventy-nine? **158**   20 How many is three times eighty-nine? **267**

21 What number is four times ninety-two? **368**   22 How many is 709 multiplied by 5? **3545**

23 If three sandwiches are to be put in each lunch, how many will be needed for 58 packed lunches? **174**   24 There are seven days in one week. How many days are there in forty-nine weeks? **343 days**

25 If one metre of P. V. C. covers eight library books, how many should be covered by one hundred and five metres? **840**   26 If there are nine balls in a box, how many will there be in one hundred and forty-four boxes? **1296 balls**

Using the terms "multiply", "multiplied by", "how many?" and "one gross".

PREPARING FOR MULTIPLICATION
Time for Table
3½ minutes

Work across the page

Extending addition (+):

A	24+ 8 = 32	24+10 = 34	25+ 7 = 32	27+ 9 = 36	28+10 = 38
B	30+11 = 41	32+ 9 = 41	36+ 8 = 44	42+ 9 = 51	45+10 = 55
C	48+ 9 = 57	49+ 8 = 57	54+11 = 65	56+ 7 = 63	60+11 = 71
D	56+ 9 = 65	63+ 7 = 70	64+ 8 = 72	63+ 9 = 72	63+11 = 74
E	72+ 8 = 80	81+ 9 = 90	64+10 = 74	72+11 = 83	96+ 4 =100
F	99+ 3 =102	90+10 =100	81+10 = 91	96+ 5 =101	99+ 6 =105
G	96+ 9 =105	99+10 =109	108+ 4 =112	96+11 =107	108+ 8 =116

MULTIPLICATION TABLE: 3
Time for Table
2½ minutes

Multiply (×):

H	10×2=20	10×3 =30	10×0 = 0	11×2 =22	12×2 = 24
I	11×3 =33	10×4 =40	11×4 =44	12×3 =36	12×4 = 48
J	10×5 =50	10×6 =60	11×5 =55	12×5 =60	11×6 = 66
K	10×7 =70	10×8 =80	11×7 =77	12×6 =72	12×7 = 84
L	11×8 =88	12×8 =96	10×9 =90	11×9 =99	12×9 =108

Multiply (×):

A	23 ×9 = 207	23 ×10 = 230	32 ×10 = 320	33 ×11 = 363	42 ×10 = 420	51 ×11 = 561
B	26 ×10 = 260	37 ×10 = 370	24 ×11 = 264	16 ×11 = 1·76	22 ×12 = 264	31 ×12 = 372
C	27 ×11 = 297	44 ×10 = 440	32 ×12 = 384	55 ×10 = 550	45 ×11 = 495	67 ×10 = 670
D	235 ×10 = 2350	316 ×11 = 3476	224 ×12 = 2688	356 ×10 = 3560	417 ×11 = 4587	344 ×12 = 4128

Practice on Table 3, no nines in multiplicand.

42

Multiply (✗):

A
256	416	517	403	306	508
× 11	× 12	× 10	× 11	× 12	× 10
2816	4992	5170	4433	3672	5080

B
406	607	515	425	788	525
× 11	× 10	× 12	× 12	× 10	× 12
4466	6070	6180	5100	7880	6300

C
523	989	367	725	825	467
× 11	× 10	× 12	× 12	× 12	× 12
5753	9890	4404	8700	9900	5604

D
678	768	638	998	742	842
× 11	× 11	× 12	× 10	× 12	× 12
7458	8448	7656	9980	8904	10104

E
788	908	407	505	805	675
× 11	× 11	× 12	× 12	× 12	× 12
8668	9988	4884	6060	9660	8100

F
954	767	867	967	975	908
× 11	× 12	× 12	× 12	× 12	× 12
10494	9204	10404	11604	11700	10896

G
693	599	639	693	895	696
× 11	× 11	× 12	× 12	× 11	× 12
7623	6589	7668	8316	9845	8352

H
799	588	689	609	709	584
× 11	× 12	× 12	× 12	× 12	× 12
8789	7056	8268	7308	8508	7008

I
999	875	884	909	984	899
× 11	× 12	× 12	× 10	× 12	× 12
10989	10500	10608	9090	11808	10788

G introduces carrying ten or more.

MULTIPLICATION WITH WORDS (3)

Write answers only

1 Multiply seven by two.   14

2 Find the product of 10×6.   60

3 Find the product of 9×10.   90

4 Twelve threes.   36

5 Nine multiplied by nine.   81

6 Find the product of 12×9.   108

Work out on paper

7 Multiply seventy-eight by five.   390

8 What number is seven times five-hundred-and-thirty-two?   3724

9 What number is equal to eight times four-hundred-and-twenty-seven?   3416

10 Find the product of eleven and two-hundred-and-nine.   2299

11 Find the product of nine and four-hundred-and-eighteen.   3762

12 What is the product of three-hundred-and-sixty-six and eleven?   4026

13 What equals nine times six-hundred-and-thirty-five?   5715

14 Find the product of twelve and three-hundred-and-eighty-four.   4608

15 If a machine can stamp 580 letters in one hour, how many will it stamp in 9 hours?   5220 letters

16 If a ship is to average 809 kilometres per day, how far will it cruise in 12 days?   9708 KM

Introduces the term "the product of".

CHECK YOUR LONG MULTIPLICATION

				Further Practice Page
A	314 × 10 = 3140	560 × 20 = 11200	405 × 60 = 24300	45 rows A & B
B	423 × 21 = 8883	419 × 22 = 9218	509 × 23 = 11707	45 rows C–F
C	207 × 24 = 4968	360 × 31 = 11160	580 × 24 = 13920	46 rows A–C
D	252 × 15 = 3780	406 × 35 = 14210	505 × 36 = 18180	46 rows D–F
E	806 × 45 = 36270	655 × 38 = 24890	859 × 47 = 40373	47 rows A–C
F	450 × 18 = 8100	780 × 65 = 50700	4080 × 85 = 346800	47 rows D–F

See pages iv and v for suggestions on how best to use this page. An alternative check page for long multiplication is printed on page 75 of the Teacher's Edition.

Multiply (×):

A
$$\begin{array}{r} 231 \\ \times\ 10 \\ \hline 2310 \end{array} \qquad \begin{array}{r} 204 \\ \times\ 10 \\ \hline 2040 \end{array} \qquad \begin{array}{r} 560 \\ \times\ 10 \\ \hline 5600 \end{array} \qquad \begin{array}{r} 780 \\ \times\ 10 \\ \hline 7800 \end{array}$$

B
$$\begin{array}{r} 426 \\ \times\ 20 \\ \hline 8520 \end{array} \qquad \begin{array}{r} 420 \\ \times\ 50 \\ \hline 21000 \end{array} \qquad \begin{array}{r} 605 \\ \times\ 60 \\ \hline 36300 \end{array} \qquad \begin{array}{r} 505 \\ \times\ 80 \\ \hline 40400 \end{array}$$

C
$$\begin{array}{r} 234 \\ \times\ 21 \\ \hline 4914 \end{array} \qquad \begin{array}{r} 174 \\ \times\ 21 \\ \hline 3654 \end{array} \qquad \begin{array}{r} 178 \\ \times\ 21 \\ \hline 3738 \end{array} \qquad \begin{array}{r} 216 \\ \times\ 31 \\ \hline 6696 \end{array}$$

D
$$\begin{array}{r} 247 \\ \times\ 31 \\ \hline 7657 \end{array} \qquad \begin{array}{r} 388 \\ \times\ 22 \\ \hline 8536 \end{array} \qquad \begin{array}{r} 519 \\ \times\ 22 \\ \hline 11418 \end{array} \qquad \begin{array}{r} 456 \\ \times\ 23 \\ \hline 10488 \end{array}$$

E
$$\begin{array}{r} 179 \\ \times\ 31 \\ \hline 5549 \end{array} \qquad \begin{array}{r} 207 \\ \times\ 23 \\ \hline 4761 \end{array} \qquad \begin{array}{r} 208 \\ \times\ 32 \\ \hline 6656 \end{array} \qquad \begin{array}{r} 409 \\ \times\ 22 \\ \hline 8998 \end{array}$$

F
$$\begin{array}{r} 608 \\ \times\ 23 \\ \hline 13984 \end{array} \qquad \begin{array}{r} 709 \\ \times\ 32 \\ \hline 22688 \end{array} \qquad \begin{array}{r} 507 \\ \times\ 23 \\ \hline 11661 \end{array} \qquad \begin{array}{r} 706 \\ \times\ 33 \\ \hline 23298 \end{array}$$

A-B Multipliers only ten or multiples of ten.
C   introduces two-figure multiplying.
E   introduces noughts difficulties.

46 **Multiply (×):**

A

	340		260		380		470
×	21	×	21	×	22	×	31
	7140		5460		8360		14570

B

	470		580		607		705
×	23	×	31	×	24	×	32
	10810		17980		14568		22560

C

	731		453		678		596
×	25	×	25	×	32	×	41
	18275		11325		21696		24436

D

	709		342		516		347
×	15	×	15	×	25	×	17
	10635		5130		12900		5899

E

	408		305		505		608
×	35	×	26	×	18	×	35
	14280		7930		9090		21280

F

	668		546		505		705
×	25	×	35	×	44	×	46
	16700		19110		22220		32430

A-B continue nought difficulties.
C-F Harder examples.

Multiply (×):

A

```
    709          806          690          780
  ×  17        ×  35        ×  43        ×  52
  12053        28210        29670        40560
```

B

```
    725          808          655          578
  ×  42        ×  45        ×  28        ×  55
  30450        36360        18340        31790
```

C

```
    589          789          825          907
  ×  38        ×  47        ×  46        ×  54
  22382        37083        37950        48978
```

D

```
    650          550          750          850
  ×  16        ×  36        ×  38        ×  48
  10400        19800        28500        40800
```

E

```
    460          680         6040         8020
  ×  45        ×  55        ×  25        ×  65
  20700        37400       151000       521300
```

F

```
   1204         2015         3050         5060
  × 160        × 236        × 206        × 402
 192640       475540       628300      2034120
```

A page for consolidation.

48

					Further Practice	
					Table	Pages
A	12 2)2 4	123 3)3 6 9	201 4)8 0 4	320 3)9 6 0	1	50
B	3 5)1 5	43 3)1 2 9	51 4)2 0 4	50 6)3 0 0	1	51
C	211 r1 3)6 3 4	51 r1 4)2 0 5	40 r1 5)2 0 1	60 r5 6)3 6 5	1	52
D	26 2)5 2	213 4)8 5 2	241 3)7 2 3	151 6)9 0 6	1	53
E	47 r2 4)1 9 0	140 r1 5)7 0 1	150 6)9 0 0	64 r3 6)3 8 7	1	54 to 56
F	168 3)5 0 4	128 5)6 4 0	115 7)8 0 5	124 r4 8)9 9 6	2	58
G	89 r1 2)1 7 9	94 r3 4)3 7 9	88 r2 6)5 3 0	47 r5 7)3 3 4	2	59 & 60
H	84 r1 7)5 8 9	75 8)6 0 0	780 r1 5)3 9 0 1	894 r6 9)8 0 5 2	2	61 & 62
I	730 r2 9)6 5 7 2	475 12)5 7 0 0	591 r1 11)6 5 0 2	96 r8 12)1 1 6 0	3	65

See pages iv and v for suggestions on how best to use this page. An alternative check page for division is printed on page 76 of the Teacher's Edition.

PREPARING FOR DIVISION
Work across the page

Take away (−):

A	13−12=1	14−12=2	16−15=1	17−15=2	17−16=1
B	19−18=1	15−12=3	17−12=5	18−15=3	18−16=2
C	19−16=3	21−18=3	23−18=5	24−20=4	25−24=1
D	27−24=3	29−24=5	33−30=3	37−36=1	38−36=2
E	26−25=1	29−25=4	19−15=4	35−30=5	39−36=3

Complete these sums

Multiply (×):

F	2×2 = 4	3×2 = 6	3×3 = 9	2×4 = 8
G	5×2 =10	3×4 =12	2×6 =12	2×4 = 8
H	4×3 =12	5×3 =15	3×6 =18	4×4 =16
I	5×4 =20	6×2 =12	5×4 =20	6×3 =18
J	5×5 =25	4×6 =24	5×6 =30	6×5 =30
K	4×6 =24	6×5 =30	5×6 =30	6×6 =36

DIVISION TABLE: 1
Write answers only

Divide (÷):

A	5÷2=2 r1	7÷2=3 r1	7÷3=2 r1	8÷3=2 r2	9÷2=4 r1
B	10÷3=3 r1	11÷2=5 r1	11÷4=2 r3	12÷4=3	13÷3=4 r1
C	13÷2=6 r1	13÷4=3 r1	14÷4=3 r2	11÷5=2 r1	13÷5=2 r3
D	16÷4=4	17÷4=4 r1	19÷4=4 r3	20÷4=5	21÷4=5 r1
E	15÷5=3	16÷5=3 r1	18÷3=6	19÷3=6 r1	20÷3=6 r2
F	22÷4=5 r2	24÷4=6	26÷4=6 r2	17÷5=3 r2	19÷5=3 r4
G	21÷5=4 r1	23÷5=4 r3	26÷5=5 r1	28÷5=5 r3	29÷5=5 r4
H	23÷4=5 r3	30÷5=6	32÷5=6 r2	14÷6=2 r2	19÷6=3 r1
I	34÷5=6 r4	22÷6=3 r4	27÷6=4 r3	33÷6=5 r3	39÷6=6 r3

Extending subtraction to 39−36.
Preparation for, and selections from, number combinations to 39÷6.

50 Divide (÷):

A $\overset{1\,2}{2)\overline{2\,4}}$ $\overset{1\,2}{3)\overline{3\,6}}$ $\overset{2\,3}{2)\overline{4\,6}}$ $\overset{2\,1}{3)\overline{6\,3}}$ $\overset{1\,1}{4)\overline{4\,4}}$

B $\overset{3\,3}{2)\overline{6\,6}}$ $\overset{2\,2}{3)\overline{6\,6}}$ $\overset{1\,2}{4)\overline{4\,8}}$ $\overset{3\,4}{2)\overline{6\,8}}$ $\overset{4\,2}{2)\overline{8\,4}}$

C $\overset{3\,1}{3)\overline{9\,3}}$ $\overset{2\,1}{4)\overline{8\,4}}$ $\overset{2\,3}{3)\overline{6\,9}}$ $\overset{2\,2}{4)\overline{8\,8}}$ $\overset{3\,3}{3)\overline{9\,9}}$

D $\overset{1\,1\,1}{3)\overline{3\,3\,3}}$ $\overset{1\,1\,2}{2)\overline{2\,2\,4}}$ $\overset{1\,2\,1}{3)\overline{3\,6\,3}}$ $\overset{2\,1\,3}{2)\overline{4\,2\,6}}$ $\overset{1\,4\,2}{2)\overline{2\,8\,4}}$

E $\overset{1\,2\,2}{3)\overline{3\,6\,6}}$ $\overset{3\,2\,1}{2)\overline{6\,4\,2}}$ $\overset{2\,2\,1}{3)\overline{6\,6\,3}}$ $\overset{3\,2\,4}{2)\overline{6\,4\,8}}$ $\overset{1\,3\,1}{3)\overline{3\,9\,3}}$

F $\overset{1\,2\,2}{4)\overline{4\,8\,8}}$ $\overset{2\,3\,2}{3)\overline{6\,9\,6}}$ $\overset{2\,1\,2}{4)\overline{8\,4\,8}}$ $\overset{3\,3\,2}{3)\overline{9\,9\,6}}$ $\overset{2\,2\,1}{4)\overline{8\,8\,4}}$

G $\overset{1\,0\,1}{2)\overline{2\,0\,2}}$ $\overset{1\,0\,2}{3)\overline{3\,0\,6}}$ $\overset{3\,0\,2}{2)\overline{6\,0\,4}}$ $\overset{1\,0\,2}{4)\overline{4\,0\,8}}$ $\overset{2\,0\,3}{3)\overline{6\,0\,9}}$

H $\overset{4\,0\,3}{2)\overline{8\,0\,6}}$ $\overset{3\,0\,3}{3)\overline{9\,0\,9}}$ $\overset{2\,0\,2}{4)\overline{8\,0\,8}}$ $\overset{1\,2\,0}{4)\overline{4\,8\,0}}$ $\overset{3\,4\,0}{2)\overline{6\,8\,0}}$

I $\overset{2\,2\,0}{3)\overline{6\,6\,0}}$ $\overset{4\,3\,0}{2)\overline{8\,6\,0}}$ $\overset{3\,2\,0}{3)\overline{9\,6\,0}}$ $\overset{2\,1\,0}{4)\overline{8\,4\,0}}$ $\overset{3\,3\,0}{3)\overline{9\,9\,0}}$

J $\overset{2\,2\,0}{4)\overline{8\,8\,0}}$ $\overset{2\,0\,0}{3)\overline{6\,0\,0}}$ $\overset{4\,0\,0}{2)\overline{8\,0\,0}}$ $\overset{3\,0\,0}{3)\overline{9\,0\,0}}$ $\overset{2\,0\,0}{4)\overline{8\,0\,0}}$

A—F No carrying: no remainders: no noughts.
G—J No carrying: no remainders: noughts in dividend.

Divide (÷):

A $2)\overline{1\,2}$ (6) $4)\overline{1\,2}$ (3) $3)\overline{1\,5}$ (5) $5)\overline{1\,5}$ (3) $4)\overline{1\,6}$ (4)

B $6)\overline{1\,8}$ (3) $3)\overline{1\,8}$ (6) $4)\overline{2\,4}$ (6) $5)\overline{2\,5}$ (5) $6)\overline{2\,4}$ (4)

C $4)\overline{2\,0}$ (5) $5)\overline{2\,0}$ (4) $5)\overline{3\,0}$ (6) $6)\overline{3\,0}$ (5) $6)\overline{3\,6}$ (6)

D $2)\overline{1\,2\,2}$ (61) $2)\overline{1\,2\,6}$ (63) $3)\overline{1\,2\,6}$ (42) $6)\overline{1\,2\,6}$ (21) $3)\overline{1\,5\,6}$ (52)

E $4)\overline{1\,2\,8}$ (32) $5)\overline{1\,5\,5}$ (31) $4)\overline{1\,6\,8}$ (42) $3)\overline{1\,8\,3}$ (61) $2)\overline{1\,0\,4}$ (52)

F $5)\overline{1\,0\,5}$ (21) $4)\overline{2\,0\,8}$ (52) $5)\overline{2\,0\,5}$ (41) $6)\overline{1\,8\,6}$ (31) $4)\overline{2\,4\,8}$ (62)

G $5)\overline{2\,5\,5}$ (51) $6)\overline{2\,4\,6}$ (41) $5)\overline{3\,0\,5}$ (61) $6)\overline{3\,0\,6}$ (51) $6)\overline{3\,6\,6}$ (61)

H $2)\overline{8\,0}$ (40) $3)\overline{9\,0}$ (30) $2)\overline{1\,2\,0}$ (60) $3)\overline{1\,5\,0}$ (50) $4)\overline{1\,6\,0}$ (40)

I $5)\overline{1\,5\,0}$ (30) $4)\overline{2\,4\,0}$ (60) $5)\overline{2\,5\,0}$ (50) $6)\overline{1\,8\,0}$ (30) $6)\overline{2\,4\,0}$ (40)

J $4)\overline{2\,0\,0}$ (50) $5)\overline{2\,0\,0}$ (40) $5)\overline{3\,0\,0}$ (60) $6)\overline{3\,0\,0}$ (50) $6)\overline{3\,6\,0}$ (60)

No carrying: no remainders: divisor not contained in first figure of dividend.

52

Divide (÷):

A $2\overline{)443} = 221\,r1$ $2\overline{)645} = 322\,r1$ $3\overline{)635} = 211\,r2$ $3\overline{)668} = 222\,r2$ $4\overline{)125} = 31\,r1$

B $5\overline{)106} = 21\,r1$ $5\overline{)107} = 21\,r2$ $4\overline{)169} = 42\,r1$ $3\overline{)157} = 52\,r1$ $3\overline{)188} = 62\,r2$

C $4\overline{)205} = 51\,r1$ $4\overline{)207} = 51\,r3$ $5\overline{)157} = 31\,r2$ $6\overline{)129} = 21\,r3$ $4\overline{)209} = 52\,r1$

D $5\overline{)158} = 31\,r3$ $4\overline{)247} = 61\,r3$ $5\overline{)207} = 41\,r2$ $6\overline{)189} = 31\,r3$ $4\overline{)249} = 62\,r1$

E $5\overline{)209} = 41\,r4$ $5\overline{)258} = 51\,r3$ $5\overline{)259} = 51\,r4$ $6\overline{)249} = 41\,r3$ $5\overline{)307} = 61\,r2$

F $6\overline{)307} = 51\,r1$ $5\overline{)309} = 61\,r4$ $6\overline{)309} = 51\,r3$ $6\overline{)368} = 61\,r2$ $6\overline{)369} = 61\,r3$

G $2\overline{)121} = 60\,r1$ $3\overline{)121} = 40\,r1$ $3\overline{)152} = 50\,r2$ $3\overline{)182} = 60\,r2$ $4\overline{)123} = 30\,r3$

H $4\overline{)161} = 40\,r1$ $5\overline{)102} = 20\,r2$ $5\overline{)104} = 20\,r4$ $4\overline{)203} = 50\,r3$ $5\overline{)153} = 30\,r3$

I $5\overline{)201} = 40\,r1$ $6\overline{)185} = 30\,r5$ $6\overline{)244} = 40\,r4$ $5\overline{)254} = 50\,r4$ $5\overline{)301} = 60\,r1$

J $6\overline{)303} = 50\,r3$ $4\overline{)243} = 60\,r3$ $6\overline{)305} = 50\,r5$ $5\overline{)304} = 60\,r4$ $6\overline{)365} = 60\,r5$

A—F No carrying: remainders: no noughts in units of answer.
G—J No carrying: remainders: noughts in units of answers.

Divide (÷):

A

16	14	36	24	25
2)3 2	3)4 2	2)7 2	3)7 2	3)7 5

B

46	16	26	13	23
2)9 2	3)4 8	3)7 8	4)5 2	4)9 2

C

13	12	14	24	15
5)6 5	6)7 2	4)5 6	4)9 6	5)7 5

D

25	35	45	15	12
2)5 0	2)7 0	2)9 0	4)6 0	5)6 0

E

16	16	13	14	15
4)6 4	5)8 0	6)7 8	6)8 4	6)9 0

F

216	114	215	213	326
2)4 3 2	3)3 4 2	3)6 4 5	4)8 5 2	3)9 7 8

G

113	115	113	216	114
5)5 6 5	5)5 7 5	6)6 7 8	4)8 6 4	6)6 8 4

H

112	215	116	115	116
5)5 6 0	4)8 6 0	5)5 8 0	6)6 9 0	6)6 9 6

I

162	241	263	242	131
2)3 2 4	3)7 2 3	3)7 8 9	4)9 6 8	5)6 5 5

J

121	151	131	141	161
6)7 2 6	5)7 5 5	6)7 8 6	6)8 4 6	6)9 6 6

A—C introduce carrying: no remainders: no noughts.
D—E continue as A—C but with noughts.
F—H Carrying from tens to units only, no remainders.
I—J Carrying from hundreds to tens only, no remainders, no noughts.

54

Divide (÷):

A
$\overset{2\,6\,3}{2\overline{)5\,2\,6}}$ $\overset{2\,5\,2}{3\overline{)7\,5\,6}}$ $\overset{1\,1\,4}{5\overline{)5\,7\,0}}$ $\overset{2\,3\,2}{4\overline{)9\,2\,8}}$ $\overset{1\,6\,2}{4\overline{)6\,4\,8}}$

B
$\overset{1\,5\,2}{2\overline{)3\,0\,4}}$ $\overset{2\,5\,3}{2\overline{)5\,0\,6}}$ $\overset{3\,5\,4}{2\overline{)7\,0\,8}}$ $\overset{1\,5\,1}{4\overline{)6\,0\,4}}$ $\overset{4\,5\,4}{2\overline{)9\,0\,8}}$

C
$\overset{1\,2\,1}{5\overline{)6\,0\,5}}$ $\overset{1\,5\,2}{4\overline{)6\,0\,8}}$ $\overset{1\,4\,1}{5\overline{)7\,0\,5}}$ $\overset{1\,6\,1}{5\overline{)8\,0\,5}}$ $\overset{1\,5\,1}{6\overline{)9\,0\,6}}$

D
$\overset{1\,3\,4}{3\overline{)4\,0\,2}}$ $\overset{1\,3\,5}{3\overline{)4\,0\,5}}$ $\overset{1\,2\,6}{4\overline{)5\,0\,4}}$ $\overset{1\,2\,5}{4\overline{)5\,0\,0}}$ $\overset{1\,4\,5}{4\overline{)5\,8\,0}}$

E
$\overset{5\,5}{2\overline{)1\,1\,0}}$ $\overset{4\,5}{4\overline{)1\,8\,0}}$ $\overset{3\,4}{5\overline{)1\,7\,0}}$ $\overset{2\,5}{6\overline{)1\,5\,0}}$ $\overset{3\,5}{6\overline{)2\,1\,0}}$

F
$\overset{1\,2\,1\,r1}{5\overline{)6\,0\,6}}$ $\overset{1\,5\,1\,r2}{4\overline{)6\,0\,6}}$ $\overset{6\,6\,r2}{3\overline{)2\,0\,0}}$ $\overset{2\,3\,3\,r1}{3\overline{)7\,0\,0}}$ $\overset{1\,5\,0\,r3}{4\overline{)6\,0\,3}}$

G
$\overset{3\,0\,0}{3\overline{)9\,0\,0}}$ $\overset{2\,0\,0}{4\overline{)8\,0\,0}}$ $\overset{1\,5\,0}{4\overline{)6\,0\,0}}$ $\overset{1\,4\,0}{5\overline{)7\,0\,0}}$ $\overset{1\,5\,0}{6\overline{)9\,0\,0}}$

H
$\overset{5\,0\,r2}{4\overline{)2\,0\,2}}$ $\overset{3\,0}{5\overline{)1\,5\,0}}$ $\overset{3\,0}{6\overline{)1\,8\,0}}$ $\overset{1\,2\,0\,r3}{5\overline{)6\,0\,3}}$ $\overset{5\,0\,r5}{6\overline{)3\,0\,5}}$

I
$\overset{2\,2\,5}{4\overline{)9\,0\,0}}$ $\overset{1\,4\,0\,r4}{5\overline{)7\,0\,4}}$ $\overset{1\,0\,0\,r4}{5\overline{)5\,0\,4}}$ $\overset{3\,1\,r4}{6\overline{)1\,9\,0}}$ $\overset{3\,4\,r3}{6\overline{)2\,0\,7}}$

J
$\overset{4\,5}{6\overline{)2\,7\,0}}$ $\overset{1\,3\,0\,r1}{6\overline{)7\,8\,1}}$ $\overset{6\,0\,r2}{5\overline{)3\,0\,2}}$ $\overset{1\,5\,0\,r5}{6\overline{)9\,0\,5}}$ $\overset{1\,4\,5}{6\overline{)8\,7\,0}}$

A—C continue from p. 53, with noughts.
D—J combine all previous noughts difficulties.

DIVISION WITH WORDS (1)

Write answers only

1 How many threes make twelve? *4 threes*

2 How many fours make sixteen? *4 fours*

3 Share eighteen cakes among three people. *6 cakes each*

4 Share twenty marbles among four children. *5 marbles each*

5 How many fours make twenty-four? *6 fours*

6 Share twenty-five sweets among five children. *5 sweets each*

7 Divide twenty-three by five. *4 r3*

8 Divide twenty-seven by four. *6 r3*

9 Share twenty-four marbles among six children. *4 marbles each*

10 How many sixes make thirty? *5 sixes*

Work out on paper

11 Divide 210 children into five classes. *42 children per class*

12 How many fives in three-hundred-and-three? *60 r3*

13 Share three-hundred-and-six children equally among six 'buses. *51 children per bus*

14 A farmer is to plant 820 cabbages in five rows. How many plants will be in each row? *164 plants per row*

15 Divide two-hundred-and-seventy into six equal groups. *45 per group*

16 Share three-hundred-and-thirty-six bottles of milk equally among six classes. *56 bottles per class*

Introduces the terms "How many?", "divide" and "share".

Divide (÷):

A	66 3)198	66 r1 3)199	304 3)912	50 r2 5)252	34 6)204
B	36 5)180	42 r2 5)212	45 r2 4)182	166 r2 3)500	25 6)150
C	150 r2 4)602	140 r3 5)703	160 r1 5)801	123 r2 6)740	131 r4 6)790
D	100 r2 5)502	225 4)900	200 r3 4)803	133 r1 6)799	134 6)804
E	160 r1 4)641	150 r2 5)752	151 r4 5)759	135 6)810	160 r3 5)803
F	36 r2 5)182	33 r2 6)200	35 6)210	45 5)225	43 r4 6)262
G	55 r3 4)223	46 r4 5)234	45 r2 6)272	36 r2 6)218	46 r3 6)279
H	65 4)260	50 r3 6)303	53 r2 6)320	53 r5 6)323	55 r3 5)278
I	55 r4 5)279	56 r3 6)339	66 r4 5)334	56 5)280	65 6)390
J	66 r3 4)267	61 r4 5)309	63 r1 6)379	64 r5 6)389	66 r3 6)399

More difficult examples based on Table 1.

PREPARING FOR DIVISION
Work across the page

Time for Table
2½ + 4½ minutes

Take away (—):

A	26−21 = 5	30−28 = 2	32−27 = 5	39−35 = 4	41−35 = 6
B	52−45 = 7	53−48 = 5	51−49 = 2	60−54 = 6	62−56 = 6
C	70−63 = 7	71−64 = 7	78−72 = 6	71−63 = 8	89−81 = 8

Complete these sums:

Multiply (✕):

D	2×7 = 14	7×3 = 21	8×2 = 16	3×7 = 21
E	7×4 = 28	8×3 = 24	2×9 = 18	9×2 = 18
F	9×3 = 27	5×7 = 35	5×7 = 35	4×8 = 32
G	4×9 = 36	4×9 = 36	8×5 = 40	7×6 = 42
H	5×8 = 40	6×7 = 42	7×7 = 49	6×8 = 48
I	6×8 = 48	8×8 = 64	9×6 = 54	6×9 = 54
J	9×6 = 54	8×7 = 56	7×8 = 56	9×7 = 63
K	9×8 = 72	8×9 = 72	9×7 = 63	9×9 = 81

DIVISION TABLE: 2
Write answers only

Time for Table
8 minutes

Divide (÷):

A	14÷2 = 7	16÷2 = 8	21÷3 = 7	17÷8 = 2 r1	18÷7 = 2 r4
B	19÷2 = 9 r1	20÷7 = 2 r6	29÷4 = 7 r1	28÷7 = 4	33÷7 = 4 r5
C	23÷9 = 2 r5	22÷8 = 2 r6	30÷9 = 3 r3	33÷4 = 8 r1	27÷8 = 3 r3
D	36÷4 = 9	37÷7 = 5 r2	39÷4 = 9 r3	38÷5 = 7 r3	40÷6 = 6 r4
E	37÷9 = 4 r1	41÷5 = 8 r1	41÷7 = 5 r6	43÷6 = 7 r1	41÷8 = 5 r1
F	47÷5 = 9 r2	46÷8 = 5 r6	47÷6 = 7 r5	42÷9 = 4 r6	44÷7 = 6 r2
G	50÷6 = 8 r2	50÷7 = 7 r1	53÷8 = 6 r5	48÷9 = 5 r3	58÷8 = 7 r2
H	59÷7 = 8 r3	56÷6 = 9 r2	55÷9 = 6 r1	65÷8 = 8 r1	62÷9 = 6 r8
I	66÷7 = 9 r3	73÷8 = 9 r1	70÷9 = 7 r7	79÷8 = 9 r7	80÷9 = 8 r8

Extending subtraction to 89−81. Preparation for and selections from number combinations to 89÷9.

58

Divide (÷):

A

340	200	254	167	271
2)680	3)600	2)508	3)501	2)542

B

169	266 r2	176	177	146
3)507	3)800	4)704	4)708	5)730

C

227 r1	146 r4	148	172	185
4)909	6)880	5)740	5)860	4)740

D

195	178	148 r2	114 r2	151 r3
4)780	5)890	6)890	7)800	6)909

E

188	158 r2	125 r5	138 r2	131 r3
5)940	6)950	7)880	7)968	7)920

F

127 r1	121 r2	132 r6	134 r2	113
7)890	8)970	7)930	7)940	8)904

G

135 r5	137 r1	123 r3	111	128 r4
7)950	7)960	8)987	9)999	7)900

H

111 r2	129	163 r2	129 r4	189
8)890	7)903	6)980	7)907	5)945

I

189 r4	159	123 r6	159 r5	132 r5
5)949	6)954	8)990	6)959	7)929

J

197 r2	115 r4	138 r4	124 r7	139 r6
4)790	7)809	7)970	8)999	7)979

Divisor contained in first figure of dividend, no noughts in answers.

Divide (÷):

A $\overset{7\ 3\ r1}{2\overline{)1\ 4\ 7}}$ $\overset{6\ 3}{3\overline{)1\ 8\ 9}}$ $\overset{7\ 7}{2\overline{)1\ 5\ 4}}$ $\overset{6\ 7}{3\overline{)2\ 0\ 1}}$ $\overset{8\ 8}{2\overline{)1\ 7\ 6}}$

B $\overset{9\ 9}{2\overline{)1\ 9\ 8}}$ $\overset{6\ 8}{3\overline{)2\ 0\ 4}}$ $\overset{9\ 9\ r1}{2\overline{)1\ 9\ 9}}$ $\overset{7\ 3}{3\overline{)2\ 1\ 9}}$ $\overset{4\ 8}{4\overline{)1\ 9\ 2}}$

C $\overset{7\ 6\ r1}{3\overline{)2\ 2\ 9}}$ $\overset{5\ 7}{4\overline{)2\ 2\ 8}}$ $\overset{7\ 7}{3\overline{)2\ 3\ 1}}$ $\overset{7\ 9}{3\overline{)2\ 3\ 7}}$ $\overset{5\ 8}{4\overline{)2\ 3\ 2}}$

D $\overset{8\ 3}{3\overline{)2\ 4\ 9}}$ $\overset{8\ 8\ r1}{3\overline{)2\ 6\ 5}}$ $\overset{5\ 2}{5\overline{)2\ 6\ 0}}$ $\overset{6\ 7}{4\overline{)2\ 6\ 8}}$ $\overset{6\ 7\ r2}{4\overline{)2\ 7\ 0}}$

E $\overset{7\ 5}{4\overline{)3\ 0\ 0}}$ $\overset{9\ 3\ r1}{3\overline{)2\ 8\ 0}}$ $\overset{9\ 6\ r2}{3\overline{)2\ 9\ 0}}$ $\overset{7\ 7\ r2}{4\overline{)3\ 1\ 0}}$ $\overset{6\ 1\ r4}{5\overline{)3\ 0\ 9}}$

F $\overset{9\ 9\ r1}{3\overline{)2\ 9\ 8}}$ $\overset{7\ 8}{4\overline{)3\ 1\ 2}}$ $\overset{7\ 9}{4\overline{)3\ 1\ 6}}$ $\overset{6\ 7}{5\overline{)3\ 3\ 5}}$ $\overset{8\ 2\ r2}{4\overline{)3\ 3\ 0}}$

G $\overset{8\ 7\ r1}{4\overline{)3\ 4\ 9}}$ $\overset{8\ 8\ r1}{4\overline{)3\ 5\ 3}}$ $\overset{7\ 1\ r2}{5\overline{)3\ 5\ 7}}$ $\overset{7\ 7\ r1}{5\overline{)3\ 8\ 6}}$ $\overset{8\ 9}{4\overline{)3\ 5\ 6}}$

H $\overset{7\ 8}{5\overline{)3\ 9\ 0}}$ $\overset{9\ 7\ r1}{4\overline{)3\ 8\ 9}}$ $\overset{9\ 7\ r2}{4\overline{)3\ 9\ 0}}$ $\overset{6\ 6\ r2}{6\overline{)3\ 9\ 8}}$ $\overset{9\ 8\ r2}{4\overline{)3\ 9\ 4}}$

I $\overset{7\ 8\ r2}{5\overline{)3\ 9\ 2}}$ $\overset{6\ 6\ r5}{6\overline{)4\ 0\ 1}}$ $\overset{7\ 9}{5\overline{)3\ 9\ 5}}$ $\overset{9\ 9\ r1}{4\overline{)3\ 9\ 7}}$ $\overset{6\ 7}{6\overline{)4\ 0\ 2}}$

J $\overset{9\ 5}{4\overline{)3\ 8\ 0}}$ $\overset{8\ 3\ r4}{5\overline{)4\ 1\ 9}}$ $\overset{2\ 1\ r2}{7\overline{)1\ 4\ 9}}$ $\overset{6\ 8\ r2}{6\overline{)4\ 1\ 0}}$ $\overset{2\ 3}{7\overline{)1\ 6\ 1}}$

Divisor not contained in first figure of dividend, and no noughts in answers.

60

Divide (÷):

A	85 r4 5)429	89 r1 5)446	67 r5 6)407	75 6)450	21 r3 7)150
B	96 5)480	68 r2 6)410	69 6)414	98 5)490	24 r3 7)171
C	71 r3 6)429	76 r2 6)458	99 r2 5)497	24 7)168	25 7)175
D	78 6)468	31 r1 7)218	76 r3 6)459	78 r2 6)470	32 r5 7)229
E	78 r5 6)473	33 r5 7)236	34 r2 7)240	79 r4 6)478	84 r5 6)509
F	33 r6 7)237	87 r5 6)527	34 r6 7)244	89 r3 6)537	35 r5 7)250
G	99 r2 6)596	37 r1 7)260	21 r1 8)169	38 7)266	43 r5 7)306
H	45 r2 7)317	13 8)104	47 r4 7)333	22 r2 8)178	22 r4 8)180
I	23 8)184	12 9)108	13 9)117	25 8)200	21 9)189
J	23 r6 8)190	45 r5 7)320	48 r3 7)339	24 9)216	26 r7 8)215

Continues as page 59.

Divide (÷):

A
$$7\overline{)340}\ \ 48\text{ r}4$$
$$7\overline{)400}\ \ 57\text{ r}1$$
$$8\overline{)240}\ \ 30$$
$$7\overline{)406}\ \ 58$$
$$9\overline{)270}\ \ 30$$

B
$$8\overline{)330}\ \ 41\text{ r}2$$
$$8\overline{)406}\ \ 50\text{ r}6$$
$$7\overline{)410}\ \ 58\text{ r}4$$
$$7\overline{)420}\ \ 60$$
$$9\overline{)205}\ \ 22\text{ r}7$$

C
$$8\overline{)261}\ \ 32\text{ r}5$$
$$9\overline{)220}\ \ 24\text{ r}4$$
$$9\overline{)222}\ \ 24\text{ r}6$$
$$8\overline{)268}\ \ 33\text{ r}4$$
$$8\overline{)270}\ \ 33\text{ r}6$$

D
$$7\overline{)426}\ \ 60\text{ r}6$$
$$7\overline{)458}\ \ 65\text{ r}3$$
$$8\overline{)320}\ \ 40$$
$$8\overline{)300}\ \ 37\text{ r}4$$
$$7\overline{)469}\ \ 67$$

E
$$7\overline{)560}\ \ 80$$
$$9\overline{)450}\ \ 50$$
$$8\overline{)305}\ \ 38\text{ r}1$$
$$7\overline{)535}\ \ 76\text{ r}3$$
$$7\overline{)630}\ \ 90$$

F
$$8\overline{)400}\ \ 50$$
$$8\overline{)370}\ \ 46\text{ r}2$$
$$7\overline{)589}\ \ 84\text{ r}1$$
$$9\overline{)490}\ \ 54\text{ r}4$$
$$7\overline{)608}\ \ 86\text{ r}6$$

G
$$8\overline{)470}\ \ 58\text{ r}6$$
$$9\overline{)504}\ \ 56$$
$$9\overline{)608}\ \ 67\text{ r}5$$
$$8\overline{)510}\ \ 63\text{ r}6$$
$$7\overline{)492}\ \ 70\text{ r}2$$

H
$$9\overline{)940}\ \ 104\text{ r}4$$
$$9\overline{)633}\ \ 70\text{ r}3$$
$$8\overline{)880}\ \ 110$$
$$9\overline{)950}\ \ 105\text{ r}5$$
$$8\overline{)720}\ \ 90$$

I
$$9\overline{)720}\ \ 80$$
$$9\overline{)955}\ \ 106\text{ r}1$$
$$8\overline{)806}\ \ 100\text{ r}6$$
$$9\overline{)810}\ \ 90$$
$$9\overline{)769}\ \ 85\text{ r}4$$

J
$$7\overline{)763}\ \ 109$$
$$8\overline{)856}\ \ 107$$
$$9\overline{)960}\ \ 106\text{ r}6$$
$$8\overline{)807}\ \ 100\text{ r}7$$
$$9\overline{)980}\ \ 108\text{ r}8$$

Combining all previous steps.

62 Divide (÷):

A
$$2112 \quad 4\overline{)8448}$$
$$200 \quad 5\overline{)1000}$$
$$700 \quad 5\overline{)3500}$$
$$270 \quad 4\overline{)1080}$$
$$769\,r2 \quad 4\overline{)3078}$$

B
$$788 \quad 5\overline{)3940}$$
$$678\,r2 \quad 6\overline{)4070}$$
$$438\,r1 \quad 7\overline{)3067}$$
$$909 \quad 6\overline{)5454}$$
$$607 \quad 7\overline{)4249}$$

C
$$509 \quad 7\overline{)3563}$$
$$406 \quad 8\overline{)3248}$$
$$980 \quad 6\overline{)5880}$$
$$485 \quad 8\overline{)3880}$$
$$406 \quad 9\overline{)3654}$$

D
$$799\,r5 \quad 6\overline{)4799}$$
$$690\,r3 \quad 7\overline{)4833}$$
$$481\,r3 \quad 8\overline{)3851}$$
$$506\,r6 \quad 9\overline{)4560}$$
$$556\,r7 \quad 9\overline{)5011}$$

E
$$719\,r4 \quad 7\overline{)5037}$$
$$609 \quad 8\overline{)4872}$$
$$672\,r4 \quad 8\overline{)5380}$$
$$566\,r6 \quad 9\overline{)5100}$$
$$674\,r5 \quad 8\overline{)5397}$$

F
$$568\,r8 \quad 9\overline{)5120}$$
$$666\,r6 \quad 9\overline{)6000}$$
$$675 \quad 8\overline{)5400}$$
$$744 \quad 8\overline{)5952}$$
$$580 \quad 9\overline{)5220}$$

G
$$760 \quad 8\overline{)6080}$$
$$590 \quad 9\overline{)5310}$$
$$769\,r6 \quad 7\overline{)5389}$$
$$670 \quad 9\overline{)6030}$$
$$809 \quad 8\overline{)6472}$$

H
$$880 \quad 8\overline{)7040}$$
$$867\,r6 \quad 7\overline{)6075}$$
$$904 \quad 8\overline{)7232}$$
$$806 \quad 9\overline{)7254}$$
$$900 \quad 9\overline{)8100}$$

I
$$900\,r1 \quad 9\overline{)8101}$$
$$901\,r2 \quad 8\overline{)7210}$$
$$905\,r8 \quad 9\overline{)8153}$$
$$1011\,r2 \quad 8\overline{)8090}$$
$$910 \quad 9\overline{)8190}$$

J
$$1002 \quad 7\overline{)7014}$$
$$1070 \quad 9\overline{)9630}$$
$$1008 \quad 8\overline{)8064}$$
$$890 \quad 9\overline{)8010}$$
$$1008\,r7 \quad 9\overline{)9079}$$

Thousands in dividends, combining all previous steps.

Write answers only

1 How many threes in twenty-one?   7 threes

2 How many threes equal twenty-seven?   9 threes

3 Divide thirty by four.   7 r2

4 Share forty-five equally into five parts.   9 each part

5 How many sixes are contained in 48?   8 sixes

6 How many times can **7** be taken from 28?   4 times

7 How many times can 8 be taken from 32?   4 times

8 Divide 42 sweets equally amongst 6 children.   7 sweets each girl

9 Share fifty-six into seven equal parts.   8 each part

10 How many nines make thirty-six?   4 nines

11 Divide fifty-four into nine equal parts.   6 each part

12 How many nines are equal to sixty-three?   7 nines

13 $\frac{1}{2}$ of 12.   6

14 $\frac{1}{2}$ of 16.   8

15 $\frac{1}{3}$ of 15.   5

16 $\frac{1}{3}$ of 18.   6

17 $\frac{1}{4}$ of 20.   5

18 $\frac{1}{4}$ of 24.   6

19 $\frac{1}{3}$ of 21.   7

20 $\frac{1}{3}$ of 27.   9

21 $\frac{1}{5}$ of 25.   5

22 $\frac{1}{5}$ of 40.   8

23 $\frac{1}{4}$ of 28.   7

24 $\frac{1}{4}$ of 32.   8

25 Find one-half of eighteen.   9

26 What is one-third of twenty-four?   8

27 Make twenty-one less by one-third.   14

28 Reduce twenty-seven by one-third.   18

Revision of general terms in division, with an introduction to simple fractional quantities.

PREPARING FOR DIVISION

Work across the page

64

Time for Table
$2\frac{1}{2}+4$ minutes

Write answers only:

Take away (—):

A	$23-20=3$	$37-30=7$	$30-22=8$	$33-24=9$	$46-36=10$
B	$52-44=8$	$55-48=7$	$70-60=10$	$73-66=7$	$80-72=8$
C	$85-77=8$	$93-84=9$	$101-99=2$	$102-96=6$	$111-108=3$

Multiply (✕): Complete these sums:

D	$2\times10=20$	$11\times2=22$	$2\times12=24$	$3\times11=33$
E	$11\times4=44$	$12\times3=36$	$4\times12=48$	$12\times5=60$
F	$12\times5=60$	$6\times11=66$	$11\times7=77$	$6\times12=72$
G	$6\times12=72$	$12\times7=84$	$12\times7=84$	$8\times10=80$
H	$11\times8=88$	$8\times12=96$	$12\times8=96$	$9\times11=99$
I	$10\times9=90$	$12\times9=108$	$9\times12=108$	$9\times12=108$

DIVISION TABLE: 3

Write answers only:

Time for Table
$8\frac{1}{2}$ minutes

Divide (÷):

A	$21\div10=2\frac{1}{10}$	$23\div11=2\frac{1}{11}$	$31\div11=2\frac{9}{11}$	$37\div10=3\frac{7}{10}$	$34\div11=3\frac{1}{11}$
B	$19\div12=1\frac{7}{12}$	$22\div12=1\frac{10}{12}$	$25\div12=2\frac{1}{12}$	$30\div12=2\frac{6}{12}$	$34\div12=2\frac{10}{12}$
C	$36\div12=3$	$41\div10=4\frac{1}{10}$	$38\div12=3\frac{2}{12}$	$47\div11=4\frac{3}{11}$	$41\div12=3\frac{5}{12}$
D	$47\div12=3\frac{11}{12}$	$51\div12=4\frac{3}{12}$	$56\div10=5\frac{6}{10}$	$57\div12=4\frac{9}{12}$	$60\div12=5$
E	$62\div11=5\frac{7}{11}$	$62\div12=5\frac{2}{12}$	$70\div12=5\frac{10}{12}$	$73\div12=6\frac{1}{12}$	$70\div11=6\frac{4}{11}$
F	$80\div12=6\frac{8}{12}$	$83\div12=6\frac{11}{12}$	$85\div10=8\frac{5}{10}$	$87\div12=7\frac{3}{12}$	$90\div12=7\frac{6}{12}$
G	$90\div11=8\frac{2}{11}$	$93\div12=7\frac{9}{12}$	$95\div8=11\frac{7}{8}$	$96\div12=8$	$98\div11=8\frac{10}{11}$
H	$99\div12=8\frac{3}{12}$	$100\div12=8\frac{4}{12}$	$99\div10=9\frac{9}{10}$	$100\div9=11\frac{1}{9}$	$102\div12=8\frac{6}{12}$
I	$105\div12=8\frac{9}{12}$	$110\div12=9\frac{2}{12}$	$101\div11=9\frac{2}{11}$	$112\div12=9\frac{4}{12}$	$118\div12=9\frac{10}{12}$

Preparations for, and extension of number combinations to $119\div12$.

Divide (÷):

A
$1271\frac{3}{7}$ — $7)\overline{8900}$ $1090\frac{1}{8}$ — $8)\overline{8721}$ $1094\frac{1}{9}$ — $9)\overline{9847}$ 809 — $8)\overline{6472}$ $859\frac{7}{9}$ — $9)\overline{7738}$

B
$889\frac{4}{9}$ — $9)\overline{8005}$ 100 — $10)\overline{1000}$ 100 — $11)\overline{1100}$ $950\frac{3}{10}$ — $10)\overline{9503}$ $418\frac{2}{11}$ — $11)\overline{4600}$

C
203 — $12)\overline{2436}$ $134\frac{1}{12}$ — $12)\overline{1609}$ 120 — $9)\overline{1080}$ $150\frac{1}{12}$ — $12)\overline{1801}$ $162\frac{6}{12}$ — $12)\overline{1950}$

D
428 — $11)\overline{4708}$ $806\frac{1}{10}$ — $10)\overline{8061}$ $254\frac{2}{12}$ — $12)\overline{3050}$ $277\frac{9}{12}$ — $12)\overline{3333}$ 546 — $11)\overline{6006}$

E
970 — $10)\overline{9700}$ $364\frac{1}{12}$ — $12)\overline{4369}$ 375 — $12)\overline{4500}$ $362\frac{8}{11}$ — $11)\overline{3990}$ $450\frac{1}{12}$ — $12)\overline{5401}$

F
$908\frac{2}{10}$ — $10)\overline{9082}$ 392 — $11)\overline{4312}$ $184\frac{2}{12}$ — $12)\overline{2210}$ $190\frac{1}{12}$ — $12)\overline{2281}$ 285 — $12)\overline{3420}$

G
393 — $12)\overline{4716}$ $686\frac{1}{12}$ — $12)\overline{8233}$ $693\frac{5}{11}$ — $11)\overline{7628}$ $587\frac{3}{11}$ — $11)\overline{6460}$ $694\frac{2}{12}$ — $12)\overline{8330}$

H
$900\frac{1}{9}$ — $9)\overline{8101}$ 695 — $12)\overline{8340}$ $783\frac{7}{12}$ — $12)\overline{9403}$ $900\frac{1}{10}$ — $10)\overline{9001}$ 84 — $12)\overline{1008}$

I
$86\frac{8}{12}$ — $12)\overline{1040}$ $92\frac{3}{12}$ — $12)\overline{1107}$ $99\frac{1}{11}$ — $11)\overline{1090}$ $96\frac{5}{12}$ — $12)\overline{1157}$ $97\frac{6}{12}$ — $12)\overline{1170}$

J
$181\frac{9}{11}$ — $11)\overline{2000}$ $108\frac{4}{12}$ — $12)\overline{1300}$ $100\frac{2}{12}$ — $12)\overline{1202}$ $100\frac{1}{11}$ — $11)\overline{1101}$ $99\frac{11}{12}$ — $12)\overline{1199}$

A—E Combines all previous steps, but no carrying figure greater than 9.
F introduces carrying figure greater than 9.

FRACTIONS
Write answers only

1 $\frac{1}{2}$ of 10.　5	**2** $\frac{1}{2}$ of 16.　8	**3** $\frac{1}{3}$ of 12.　4
4 $\frac{1}{4}$ of 12.　3	**5** $\frac{1}{3}$ of 15.　5	**6** $\frac{1}{4}$ of 16.　4
7 $\frac{1}{2}$ of 18.　9	**8** $\frac{1}{3}$ of 18.　6	**9** $\frac{1}{3}$ of 21.　7
10 $\frac{1}{4}$ of 20.　5	**11** $\frac{1}{4}$ of 24.　6	**12** $\frac{1}{4}$ of 32.　8
13 $\frac{1}{4}$ of 28.　7	**14** $\frac{1}{3}$ of 24.　8	**15** $\frac{1}{3}$ of 30.　10
16 $\frac{1}{3}$ of 27.　9	**17** $\frac{1}{5}$ of 10.　2	**18** $\frac{1}{5}$ of 15.　3
19 $\frac{1}{5}$ of 25.　5	**20** $\frac{1}{6}$ of 12.　2	**21** $\frac{1}{8}$ of 16.　2
22 $\frac{1}{6}$ of 18.　3	**23** $\frac{1}{8}$ of 24.　3	**24** $\frac{1}{6}$ of 30.　5
25 $\frac{1}{8}$ of 32.　4	**26** $\frac{1}{9}$ of 18.　2	**27** $\frac{1}{6}$ of 42.　7
28 $\frac{1}{7}$ of 21.　3	**29** $\frac{1}{7}$ of 35.　5	**30** $\frac{1}{7}$ of 28.　4
31 $\frac{1}{5}$ of 35.　7	**32** $\frac{1}{7}$ of 42.　6	**33** $\frac{1}{7}$ of 56.　8
34 $\frac{1}{6}$ of 54.　9	**35** $\frac{1}{8}$ of 56.　7	**36** $\frac{1}{7}$ of 63.　9
37 $\frac{1}{3}$ of 9.　3	**38** $\frac{2}{3}$ of 9.　6	**39** $\frac{1}{5}$ of 20.　4
40 $\frac{2}{5}$ of 20.　8	**41** $\frac{3}{4}$ of 20.　15	**42** $\frac{4}{5}$ of 20.　16
43 $\frac{1}{7}$ of 14.　2	**44** $\frac{2}{7}$ of 21.　6	**45** $\frac{3}{7}$ of 28.　12
46 $\frac{1}{8}$ of 24.　3	**47** $\frac{3}{8}$ of 40.　15	**48** $\frac{5}{8}$ of 48.　30
49 $\frac{1}{9}$ of 27.　3	**50** $\frac{2}{9}$ of 36.　8	**51** $\frac{7}{9}$ of 45.　35
52 $\frac{2}{7}$ of 63.　18	**53** $\frac{5}{6}$ of 42.　35	**54** $\frac{1}{10}$ of 50.　5
55 $\frac{4}{9}$ of 54.　24	**56** $\frac{1}{12}$ of 60.　5	**57** $\frac{5}{12}$ of 72.　30
58 $\frac{6}{7}$ of 56.　48	**59** $\frac{5}{9}$ of 63.　35	**60** $\frac{7}{12}$ of 84.　49

1–36 Numerators of 1 only.
37–60 Introduces numerators up to 7.

				Further Practice
				Page

A $20\overline{)4\,0}$ ... 2 $31\overline{)6\,2}$ ... 2 $42\overline{)8\,4}$ ... 2

68 rows A–C

B $21\overline{)4\,3}$ ... 2 r1 $32\overline{)6\,6}$ ... 2 r2 $22\overline{)6\,9}$ ... 3 r3

68 rows D–G

C $60\overline{)1\,2\,0}$ ... 2 $30\overline{)1\,5\,0}$ ... 5 $40\overline{)1\,6\,0}$ ... 4

68 rows H & I

D $21\overline{)2\,3\,1}$ ... 1 1 $31\overline{)3\,7\,2}$ ... 1 2 $22\overline{)6\,8\,2}$ ... 3 1

69 rows A–C

E $30\overline{)3\,6\,3\,0}$ ... 1 2 1 $40\overline{)8\,0\,0\,0}$ ... 2 0 0 $32\overline{)6\,5\,2\,8}$ ... 2 0 4

69 rows D–F

F $31\overline{)1\,2\,7\,1}$ ... 4 1 $19\overline{)2\,2\,9\,9}$ ... 1 2 1 $74\overline{)3\,0\,1\,1\,8}$ ... 4 0 7

70 rows A–E

See pages iv and v for suggestions on how best to use this page. An alternative check page for long division is printed on page 77 of the Teacher's Edition.

68 Divide (÷):

A

$10\overline{)5\,0}\ ^{5}$ $20\overline{)4\,0}\ ^{2}$ $20\overline{)6\,0}\ ^{3}$ $30\overline{)6\,0}\ ^{2}$ $40\overline{)8\,0}\ ^{2}$

B

$11\overline{)2\,2}\ ^{2}$ $21\overline{)2\,1}\ ^{1}$ $21\overline{)4\,2}\ ^{2}$ $21\overline{)6\,3}\ ^{3}$ $22\overline{)4\,4}\ ^{2}$

C

$31\overline{)6\,2}\ ^{2}$ $22\overline{)6\,6}\ ^{3}$ $32\overline{)6\,4}\ ^{2}$ $33\overline{)6\,6}\ ^{2}$ $33\overline{)9\,9}\ ^{3}$

D

$20\overline{)2\,1}\ ^{1\ r1}$ $20\overline{)4\,1}\ ^{2\ r1}$ $21\overline{)2\,2}\ ^{1\ r1}$ $21\overline{)4\,3}\ ^{2\ r1}$ $30\overline{)6\,1}\ ^{2\ r1}$

E

$22\overline{)4\,5}\ ^{2\ r1}$ $21\overline{)2\,4}\ ^{1\ r3}$ $21\overline{)4\,4}\ ^{2\ r2}$ $31\overline{)3\,4}\ ^{1\ r3}$ $31\overline{)6\,3}\ ^{2\ r1}$

F

$30\overline{)6\,2}\ ^{2\ r2}$ $21\overline{)6\,5}\ ^{3\ r2}$ $22\overline{)4\,6}\ ^{2\ r2}$ $30\overline{)9\,3}\ ^{3\ r3}$ $22\overline{)6\,8}\ ^{3\ r2}$

G

$23\overline{)4\,7}\ ^{2\ r1}$ $22\overline{)6\,9}\ ^{3\ r3}$ $21\overline{)8\,6}\ ^{4\ r2}$ $22\overline{)8\,9}\ ^{4\ r1}$ $31\overline{)9\,6}\ ^{3\ r3}$

H

$50\overline{)1\,0\,0}\ ^{2}$ $20\overline{)1\,0\,0}\ ^{5}$ $60\overline{)1\,2\,0}\ ^{2}$ $30\overline{)1\,2\,0}\ ^{4}$ $40\overline{)1\,2\,0}\ ^{3}$

I

$20\overline{)1\,2\,0}\ ^{6}$ $50\overline{)1\,5\,0}\ ^{3}$ $30\overline{)1\,5\,0}\ ^{5}$ $40\overline{)1\,6\,0}\ ^{4}$ $20\overline{)1\,4\,0}\ ^{7}$

A—C   No remainders, easily recognisable quotients.
D—G   Single figure quotients with remainders.
H—I   Divisors and dividends multiples of ten, divisor not contained in first two figures of dividend.

Divide (÷):

A

$$20\overline{)420} = 21 \qquad 21\overline{)231} = 11 \qquad 21\overline{)441} = 21 \qquad 31\overline{)341} = 11$$

B

$$30\overline{)630} = 21 \qquad 31\overline{)651} = 21 \qquad 41\overline{)451} = 11 \qquad 41\overline{)861} = 21$$

C

$$22\overline{)242} = 11 \qquad 21\overline{)462} = 22 \qquad 22\overline{)484} = 22 \qquad 21\overline{)693} = 33$$

D

$$20\overline{)2420} = 121 \qquad 30\overline{)6930} = 231 \qquad 21\overline{)4662} = 222 \qquad 32\overline{)3872} = 121$$

E

$$20\overline{)400} = 20 \qquad 40\overline{)800} = 20 \qquad 30\overline{)9000} = 300 \qquad 21\overline{)2226} = 106$$

F

$$31\overline{)3224} = 104 \qquad 22\overline{)2860} = 130 \qquad 30\overline{)6090} = 203 \qquad 31\overline{)6293} = 203$$

A-C No noughts in answers: no remainders.
D As **A-C** with thousands, hundreds, tens and units.
E-F Noughts in answers, but no remainders.

70 Divide (÷):

A

$$\overset{3\ 0\ 6}{21\overline{)6\ 4\ 2\ 6}} \qquad \overset{2\ 1\ 1}{23\overline{)4\ 8\ 5\ 3}} \qquad \overset{2\ 1\ 1}{24\overline{)5\ 0\ 6\ 4}} \qquad \overset{1\ 0\ 3\ \text{r}2}{41\overline{)4\ 2\ 2\ 5}}$$

B

$$\overset{5\ 1}{31\overline{)1\ 5\ 8\ 1}} \qquad \overset{4\ 0}{32\overline{)1\ 2\ 8\ 0}} \qquad \overset{4\ 0\ \text{r}1}{31\overline{)1\ 2\ 4\ 1}} \qquad \overset{7\ 0\ \text{r}10}{23\overline{)1\ 6\ 2\ 0}}$$

C

$$\overset{5\ 4\ \text{r}12}{22\overline{)1\ 2\ 0\ 0}} \qquad \overset{3\ 1\ \text{r}17}{44\overline{)1\ 3\ 8\ 1}} \qquad \overset{3\ 0\ \text{r}23}{35\overline{)1\ 0\ 7\ 3}} \qquad \overset{2\ 1\ \text{r}54}{55\overline{)1\ 2\ 0\ 9}}$$

D

$$\overset{1\ 2\ 0\ \text{r}10}{43\overline{)5\ 1\ 7\ 0}} \qquad \overset{1\ 1\ 0\ \text{r}3}{19\overline{)2\ 0\ 9\ 3}} \qquad \overset{1\ 3\ 1\ \text{r}15}{29\overline{)3\ 8\ 1\ 4}} \qquad \overset{2\ 2\ 2\ \text{r}5}{18\overline{)4\ 0\ 0\ 1}}$$

E

$$\overset{2\ 3\ 0\ \text{r}31}{39\overline{)9\ 0\ 0\ 1}} \qquad \overset{3\ 0\ 9\ \text{r}1}{54\overline{)1\ 6\ 6\ 8\ 7}} \qquad \overset{4\ 2\ 3\ \text{r}25}{73\overline{)3\ 0\ 9\ 0\ 4}} \qquad \overset{4\ 7\ 7\ \text{r}8}{84\overline{)4\ 0\ 0\ 7\ 6}}$$

More difficult examples, including remainders.
B introduces examples having tens figure of divisor greater than the first figure of dividend.
D introduces the "teens", etc.

TIMES FOR TABLES

A suggested time for completing each table is printed on it in red in this Teacher's Edition.

The times suggested have been found as follows:

Addition and Subtraction Tables 1–3 }
Multiplication and Division Table 1 } performance by average children aged eight.

All other tables { performance by average children aged nine.

Teachers will need to adjust these suggested times to the age and ability of their pupils. For older children, a progressively shorter time performance should be expected and obtained. Clearly also, a bright child of eight may be expected to take less time than an equally bright child of seven, but about the same time as an average child of nine.

THE WORD SUMS

Exercises in words are placed at appropriate places in this book. When used for class work, these pages make sure that the child becomes familiar with the vocabulary used at that stage of the work. These pages are also important for remedial work, as they enable the child to pick up the threads again far more easily when returning to the problems in the ordinary textbook.

A NOTE ABOUT COPYRIGHT

✚ ✚ ✚ **CHECK YOUR ADDITION** ✚ ✚ ✚

✚

						Further Practice	
						Table	**Pages**
A	2 +3 — 5	0 +4 — 4	5 +2 — 7	14 +63 — 77	38 +50 — 88	1	2 & 3
B	2 +19 — 21	4 +27 — 31	15 +25 — 40	37 +13 — 50	68 +29 — 97	2	4 & 5
C	11 23 11 — 45	12 10 25 — 47	23 12 16 — 51	17 30 8 — 55	40 6 39 — 85	2	6
D	13 23 14 — 50	35 21 63 — 119	23 40 47 — 110	35 5 60 — 100	67 2 87 — 156	2	7 to 9
E	24 15 72 — 111	43 59 80 — 182	65 78 44 — 187	88 54 8 — 150	79 85 36 — 200	3	10 & 11
F	38 45 27 — 110	46 79 96 — 221	314 107 426 — 847	547 89 100 — 736	478 99 856 — 1433	4	12 to 14
G	213 304 162 217 — 896	342 275 600 83 — 1300	437 516 80 405 — 1438	64 756 89 605 — 1514	2786 49 535 6860 — 10230	5	15 & 16
H	121 253 407 180 302 — 1263	432 560 84 607 95 — 1778	1320 4178 2645 1000 786 — 9929	5413 629 85 3070 803 — 10000	406 3517 898 92 5087 — 10000	6	17

See pages iv and v for suggestions on how to use this page.

	Further Practice	
	Table	Pages

						Table	Pages
A	$\begin{array}{r} 2 \\ -1 \\ \hline 1 \end{array}$	$\begin{array}{r} 2 \\ -2 \\ \hline 0 \end{array}$	$\begin{array}{r} 3 \\ -0 \\ \hline 3 \end{array}$	$\begin{array}{r} 0 \\ -0 \\ \hline 0 \end{array}$	$\begin{array}{r} 8 \\ -5 \\ \hline 3 \end{array}$	1	19
B	$\begin{array}{r} 35 \\ -12 \\ \hline 23 \end{array}$	$\begin{array}{r} 56 \\ -30 \\ \hline 26 \end{array}$	$\begin{array}{r} 78 \\ -43 \\ \hline 35 \end{array}$	$\begin{array}{r} 67 \\ -37 \\ \hline 30 \end{array}$	$\begin{array}{r} 89 \\ -84 \\ \hline 5 \end{array}$	1	20
C	$\begin{array}{r} 10 \\ -6 \\ \hline 4 \end{array}$	$\begin{array}{r} 30 \\ -5 \\ \hline 25 \end{array}$	$\begin{array}{r} 80 \\ -48 \\ \hline 32 \end{array}$	$\begin{array}{r} 72 \\ -37 \\ \hline 35 \end{array}$	$\begin{array}{r} 92 \\ -66 \\ \hline 26 \end{array}$	2	21 & 22
D	$\begin{array}{r} 82 \\ -73 \\ \hline 9 \end{array}$	$\begin{array}{r} 420 \\ -210 \\ \hline 210 \end{array}$	$\begin{array}{r} 807 \\ -505 \\ \hline 302 \end{array}$	$\begin{array}{r} 620 \\ -318 \\ \hline 302 \end{array}$	$\begin{array}{r} 982 \\ -334 \\ \hline 648 \end{array}$	2	23
E	$\begin{array}{r} 410 \\ -290 \\ \hline 120 \end{array}$	$\begin{array}{r} 607 \\ -437 \\ \hline 170 \end{array}$	$\begin{array}{r} 523 \\ -447 \\ \hline 76 \end{array}$	$\begin{array}{r} 700 \\ -605 \\ \hline 95 \end{array}$	$\begin{array}{r} 803 \\ -86 \\ \hline 717 \end{array}$	2	24 to 26
F	$\begin{array}{r} 530 \\ -280 \\ \hline 250 \end{array}$	$\begin{array}{r} 645 \\ -576 \\ \hline 69 \end{array}$	$\begin{array}{r} 400 \\ -396 \\ \hline 4 \end{array}$	$\begin{array}{r} 756 \\ -698 \\ \hline 58 \end{array}$	$\begin{array}{r} 900 \\ -93 \\ \hline 807 \end{array}$	3	27 & 28
G	$\begin{array}{r} 3214 \\ -1508 \\ \hline 1706 \end{array}$	$\begin{array}{r} 5004 \\ -4094 \\ \hline 910 \end{array}$	$\begin{array}{r} 6000 \\ -5093 \\ \hline 907 \end{array}$	$\begin{array}{r} 72094 \\ -6095 \\ \hline 65999 \end{array}$	$\begin{array}{r} 80020 \\ -70994 \\ \hline 9026 \end{array}$	3	30

See pages iv and v for suggestions on how to use this page.

					Further Practice	
					Table	Pages
A	$\begin{array}{r} 21 \\ \times\ 2 \\ \hline 42 \end{array}$	$\begin{array}{r} 23 \\ \times\ 3 \\ \hline 69 \end{array}$	$\begin{array}{r} 60 \\ \times\ 4 \\ \hline 240 \end{array}$	$\begin{array}{r} 50 \\ \times\ 6 \\ \hline 300 \end{array}$	1	32
B	$\begin{array}{r} 41 \\ \times\ 5 \\ \hline 205 \end{array}$	$\begin{array}{r} 16 \\ \times\ 2 \\ \hline 32 \end{array}$	$\begin{array}{r} 45 \\ \times\ 6 \\ \hline 270 \end{array}$	$\begin{array}{r} 66 \\ \times\ 5 \\ \hline 330 \end{array}$	1	33 & 34
C	$\begin{array}{r} 38 \\ \times\ 3 \\ \hline 114 \end{array}$	$\begin{array}{r} 58 \\ \times\ 7 \\ \hline 406 \end{array}$	$\begin{array}{r} 75 \\ \times\ 8 \\ \hline 600 \end{array}$	$\begin{array}{r} 78 \\ \times\ 9 \\ \hline 702 \end{array}$	2	36 & 37
D	$\begin{array}{r} 501 \\ \times\ 4 \\ \hline 2004 \end{array}$	$\begin{array}{r} 215 \\ \times\ 6 \\ \hline 1290 \end{array}$	$\begin{array}{r} 470 \\ \times\ 3 \\ \hline 1410 \end{array}$	$\begin{array}{r} 604 \\ \times\ 5 \\ \hline 3020 \end{array}$	2	38
E	$\begin{array}{r} 245 \\ \times\ 3 \\ \hline 735 \end{array}$	$\begin{array}{r} 689 \\ \times\ 4 \\ \hline 2756 \end{array}$	$\begin{array}{r} 897 \\ \times\ 7 \\ \hline 6279 \end{array}$	$\begin{array}{r} 989 \\ \times\ 9 \\ \hline 8901 \end{array}$	2	39
F	$\begin{array}{r} 206 \\ \times\ 10 \\ \hline 2060 \end{array}$	$\begin{array}{r} 546 \\ \times\ 11 \\ \hline 6006 \end{array}$	$\begin{array}{r} 625 \\ \times\ 12 \\ \hline 7500 \end{array}$	$\begin{array}{r} 837 \\ \times\ 12 \\ \hline 10044 \end{array}$	3	41 & 42
G	$\begin{array}{r} 391 \\ \times\ 11 \\ \hline 4301 \end{array}$	$\begin{array}{r} 799 \\ \times\ 11 \\ \hline 8789 \end{array}$	$\begin{array}{r} 409 \\ \times\ 12 \\ \hline 4908 \end{array}$	$\begin{array}{r} 889 \\ \times\ 12 \\ \hline 10668 \end{array}$	3	42 G

See pages iv and v for suggestions on how to use this page.

CHECK YOUR
LONG MULTIPLICATION

75

				Further Practice Pages

A

```
    132          306          505
  ×  10        ×  30        ×  60
  ------       ------       -------
   1320         9180         30300
```
45 rows A & B

B

```
    213          378          609
  ×  21        ×  22        ×  31
  ------       ------       -------
   4473         8316         18879
```
45 rows C–F

C

```
    205          350          708
  ×  21        ×  42        ×  32
  ------       -------      -------
   4305         14700        22656
```
46 rows A–C

D

```
    416          398          505
  ×  25        ×  24        ×  46
  -------      ------       -------
   10400         9552        23230
```
46 rows D–F

E

```
    374          560          785
  ×  15        ×  17        ×  38
  ------       ------       -------
   5610         9520         29830
```
47 rows A–C

F

```
    560         6050         4080
  ×  35        ×  26        × 305
  ------       -------      --------
   19600        157300       1244400
```
47 rows D–F

See pages iv and v for suggestions on how to use this page.

76

				Further Practice	
				Table	Pages
A	32 $3\overline{)96}$	342 $2\overline{)684}$	103 $3\overline{)309}$	120 $4\overline{)480}$	1	50
B	4 $4\overline{)16}$	4 $5\overline{)20}$	30 $6\overline{)180}$	50 $6\overline{)300}$	1	51
C	$321\,r1$ $2\overline{)643}$	$62\,r1$ $3\overline{)187}$	$30\,r1$ $5\overline{)151}$	$60\,r4$ $6\overline{)364}$	1	52
D	26 $2\overline{)52}$	35 $2\overline{)70}$	214 $4\overline{)856}$	141 $6\overline{)846}$	1	53
E	153 $3\overline{)459}$	26 $4\overline{)104}$	$160\,r2$ $5\overline{)802}$	$63\,r2$ $6\overline{)380}$	1	54 to 56
F	$126\,r1$ $4\overline{)505}$	$134\,r2$ $7\overline{)940}$	$100\,r7$ $9\overline{)907}$	$122\,r4$ $8\overline{)980}$	2	58
G	$65\,r1$ $3\overline{)196}$	$60\,r3$ $5\overline{)303}$	$42\,r6$ $7\overline{)300}$	$32\,r4$ $8\overline{)260}$	2	59 & 60
H	$92\,r6$ $7\overline{)650}$	$88\,r2$ $8\overline{)706}$	$715\,r2$ $7\overline{)5007}$	$889\,r7$ $9\overline{)8008}$	2	61 & 62
I	$800\,r5$ $9\overline{)7205}$	$340\,r6$ $12\overline{)4086}$	$90\,r10$ $11\overline{)1000}$	$90\,r10$ $12\overline{)1090}$	3	65

See pages iv and v for suggestions on how best to use this page.

CHECK YOUR
LONG DIVISION

77

				Further Practice Pages

A

$$31\overline{)6\,2}^{\;2} \qquad 20\overline{)6\,0}^{\;3} \qquad 21\overline{)8\,4}^{\;4}$$

68 rows A–C

B

$$20\overline{)4\,2}^{\;2\,r2} \qquad 31\overline{)6\,4}^{\;2\,r2} \qquad 23\overline{)6\,9}^{\;3}$$

68 rows D–G

C

$$20\overline{)1\,0\,0}^{\;5} \qquad 30\overline{)1\,8\,0}^{\;6} \qquad 70\overline{)1\,4\,0}^{\;2}$$

68 rows H & I

D

$$20\overline{)2\,2\,0}^{\;1\,1} \qquad 22\overline{)4\,6\,2}^{\;2\,1} \qquad 32\overline{)6\,7\,2}^{\;2\,1}$$

69 rows A–C

E

$$21\overline{)4\,4\,5\,2}^{\;2\,1\,2} \qquad 30\overline{)9\,0\,6\,0}^{\;3\,0\,2} \qquad 41\overline{)8\,2\,8\,2}^{\;2\,0\,2}$$

69 rows D–F

70 rows A–F

F

$$31\overline{)1\,2\,8\,0}^{\;4\,1\,r9} \qquad 43\overline{)5\,0\,0\,0}^{\;1\,1\,6\,r12} \qquad 68\overline{)2\,1\,2\,0}^{\;3\,1\,r12}$$

See pages iv and v for suggestions on how best to use this page.

➕ ➖ **CHECK THE FOUR RULES** ✖️ ➗

	Other Checks
	Pages

Add (+):

➕

A

1 5	3 6	3 5 4	6 2 7 8
3 0	4 7	6 9	5 6
1 8	2 4	6 8 0	9 0 6
6 3	1 0 7	1 1 0 3	2 7 8 0
			1 0 0 2 0

1 & 72

Subtract (−):

➖

B

7 6	6 0	4 2 5	8 0 0 3
−4 3	−2 9	−2 3 0	−7 0 9 5
3 3	3 1	1 9 5	9 0 8

18 & 73

Multiply (×):

C

3 4	5 0	5 6 7	8 5 9
× 3	× 6	× 9	× 1 2
1 0 2	3 0 0	5 1 0 3	1 0 3 0 8

31 & 74

✖️

D

3 0 4	7 6 5	4 6 8 0
× 3 0	× 2 8	× 7 5
9 1 2 0	2 1 4 2 0	3 5 1 0 0 0

44 & 75

Divide (÷):

E

$$3)\overline{6\,0\,9} = 203 \qquad 7)\overline{4\,0\,0} = 57\,r1 \qquad 9)\overline{2\,0\,7\,6} = 230\,r6 \qquad 12)\overline{1\,1\,8\,9} = 99\,r1$$

48 & 76

➗

F

$$50)\overline{1\,5\,0} = 3 \qquad 31)\overline{6\,5\,1} = 21 \qquad 63)\overline{3\,0\,7\,0\,2} = 487\,r21$$

67 & 77

See pages iv and v for suggestions on how best to use this page